Rife's Great Discovery

Why "Resonant Frequency" Therapy Is Kept Hidden From Public Awareness

Royal Rife

By Barry Lynes

ISBN: 978-0-9882437-9-8

Published by:
BioMed Publishing Group, LLC
PO BOX 550531
South Lake Tahoe CA 96155

To order additional copies of this book and see our selection of Rife-related books & DVDs, please visit:

www.BioMedPublishers.com

"If you have never heard of Rife before, be prepared to be angered and incredulous at what this great man achieved for all of us only to have it practically driven from the face of the planet. When you thoroughly understand Rife's achievements, you may well decide that his was one of the most gifted, versatile, scientific minds in human history."

Jeff Rense

"Having spent every dime I earned in my research for the benefit of mankind, I have ended up a pauper, but I achieved the impossible and would do it again."

Royal Rife

"Rife had advanced biology and biophysics a century in one jump ... He died without ever being vindicated for his miraculous, world-shaking discoveries."

Tom Beardon

"Rife frequency healing is named after its inventor, Royal "Raymond Rife. After this technology was enthusiastically embraced by some of the most prominent physicians and scientists of the 1930s and 1940s, it was driven underground by the pharmaceutical interests and the American Medical Association (AMA). Only in the last couple of decades has Rife technology emerged again in popularity ...

"In countries outside the United States ... Rife technology is seriously researched and publicized. Its legal status as a medical treatment means that the technology is freely used in clinics and doctors' offices. In North America, open minded medical practitioners and health seekers have a more difficult time ... because after the 1940s, the FDA quashed this technology."

("Healing With Electromedicine and Sound Therapies, Part Two," by Nenah Sylver, Ph.D., Townsend Letter For Doctors, April 2008.)

"Dr. Arthur Yale of San Diego reported that with the aid of the Rife ray he has succeeded in curing a number of cases of malignant cancer in which patients had been told they had only a limited time in which to live ...

" 'The effect of the ray on all malignant growth,' the physician declared, 'is so remarkable ... advancing what evidently promises to be the first positive treatment for the ever increasing curse of cancer' ..."

("New Cancer Foe Hailed : Powerful Ray Credited With Killing Germs," Los Angeles Times, May 18, 1940.)

Rife's Great Discovery

Why "Resonant Frequency" Therapy

Is Kept Hidden From Public Awareness

By Barry Lynes

Dedicated to Cynthia and Tom

for their consistent skill and support

"The cancer industry has grown to be a financial Goliath worth hundreds of billions of dollars in profits each year ... the cancer industry also includes huge salaries, perks and other expenses in numerous government agencies and non-profit organizations. **The inescapable reality is that all those profits, salaries, and perks can only be maintained, much less increased, if we do NOT find a cure for cancer** ...

"When you look at how cancer research continues to be misdirected ... there is an obvious conclusion. The failure to direct efforts towards finding a cure for cancer has been deliberate. As with mainstream medicine in general, greed and profits are foremost and our health takes a distant second place."

("Stopping the Cure: Why Cancer Research isn't focused on the true cause of cancer" by Tony Isaacs, thetruthaboutcancer.com)

"The Food and Drug Aministration (FDA) is responsible for regulating pharmaceutical drugs, dietary supplements, cosmetics ingredients, and livestock and agriculture operations. There are several problems with this agency, generally related to the fact that the most profitable industries in the world (Big Pharma and monster biotech firms such as Monsanto and Syngenta) have managed **to hijack the agency and are now setting policy**.

"Big Pharma directs the FDA to approve unsafe and ineffective drugs, generally by falsifying data in clinical trials. Big Pharma also directs the FDA to attack and drive out of business any competition, including doctors having success with alternative cancer treatments ..."

("Big Pharma Is Making Us Sick" by Wade Frazier, integratingdarkandlight.com)

" ... war against natural healing methods began in the 1930s and 1940s and has continued since, carried forward by power and money motivations, to establish a medical monopoly on health care -- driving out natural, inexpensive, and effective methods for treatment of disease."

("The Suppression of Dissent and Innovative Ideas in Science and Medicine," by James Demeo, organelab.org)

"There have been many cancer cures, and all have been ruthlessly and systematically suppressed with a Gestapo-like thoroughness by the cancer establishment." (Robert C. Atkins, M.D., beating-cancer-gently.com)

****

"The 'cancer establishment' is a network of extremely powerful and wealthy companies whose members sit on the boards of many non-profit organisations. They literally control and direct all cancer research within the USA and throughout the world ... Although these centres are non-profit, they serve their masters by suppressing most, if not all, non-patenable treatments in favour of the expensive treatment therapies that have wrought havoc with patients while losing the war against cancer ... we have a corrupt, self-serving and often inept government bureaucracy that protects these special interest." (Robert Willner, M.D., author *The Cancer Solution*)

****

"... there is clearly a lack of desire in the mainstream medical establishment to research alternative, natural medicines and treatments for cancer ..." (Anna Hunt, "Cancer: The Forbidden Cures," WakingTimes.com)

****

"Instances of the takeover and manipulation of science abound. The chemical / biotechnology corporations serve as a prime example. They figured out that science is the religion of the day, and taking control of science is to take control of people. They have used every means at their disposal to suppress scientific enquiry." (Dr. Nancy Swanson, "The Corruption by Science," Institute of Science in Society)

****

"What Rife was doing was using resonance to kill the virus. Everything vibrates at different frequencies. If the resonance is corret, it can be used to shatter, just as a singer can use it to break a wineglass. By finding the proper resonance, Rife was able to shatter the virus. This is why he called it the Mortal Oscillatory Rate ... All told, there were over 50 diseases that he apparently discovered cures for." (Lew Rockwell, iimetro.com)

Introduction -- The Fabulous Rife

He was solidly a genius. He found something in **nature** that had eluded countless scientists of quality who had preceded him. He discovered that disease-causing organisms of virus-size could be quickly, safely, surely and permanently destroyed by intensifying their natural, unique "Resonant Frequency." Without harming any other tissues, cells or organs! He had found a new method of healing that could replace much of chemical medicine.

This made him an enemy of the drug combines that made fortunes treating cancer and other diseases with outrageously overpriced chemo concoctions. Thus the great scientist's work had to be suppressed Not given any recognition. Not allowed to be objectively evaluated in academy settings. Not discussed in peer-reviewed science and medical journals. Too much of a threat to big financial cartels. The **annual market** for cancer drugs was in the clouds by the 2nd decade of the 21st century -- pushing **$100 billion**. And it could all be replaced by the introduction of frequency devices that would destroy the tiny, living, micro organisms filtered from human cancer tissue.

Corruption is mammoth in the drug world. Even prestigious medical journals such as *The New England Journal of Medicine* and the *BMJ* which was previously called the *British Medical Journal* have admitted that this problem substantially soils the professions of science and medicine.

However, the suppression of a great scientific discovery that could cure cancer and other terrible diseases meant that millions of people would continue dying so that a sanctioned racket continued producing profits for the industrial moguls running "Big Pharma." The only appropriate moral action would be to allow entry for the new therapy. But in times when society in general was managed by politically powerful interests and corruption of all kiinds flourished, the professions were usually intimidated and not especially characterized by moral courage. In essence, they were controlled.

Academia was silent. The news media was silent. The medical and scientific "communities" dared not break the existing taboos.

Dr. Rife was disparaged by the authorities. His scientific work had been "disproved" according to the official line, even though the statement was a bald lie. But almost everyone in a position to challenge the cover-up of his discoveries meekly "went along."

A wonderous cure for cancer and other diseases had emerged from the great discovery that humanity's health could be greatly enhanced merely by allowing the principles of "Resonant Therapy" science to be publicly advocated, openly discussed and tested. As if the society were once again honest and free to examine with integrity something new and exciting -- such as a great new field of science that would replace most of the drug medicine monopolies. Kind of like going for the Moon when American leadership was young and brave and visionary. No more.

If only Dr. Rife's discoveries were allowed to be studied and openly allowed to be used in hospitals. Perhaps the citizens should be allowed to vote on such an experimental treatment? No? Why not? Oh, that's a medical expert decision? Which means its a rigged decision which inevitably favors the established dogma, orthodoxy and career goals.

Why does that happen in a supposed democracy where individual freedom is supposed to be a fundamental element? Has the "Great Republic" faltered because its leadership class has lost its guts and now fears to deal with ugly realities and vast corruption?

In simple terms, Dr. Rife discovered that he could identify the unique frequency "signature" of a disease-causing organism of virus-size.
By **intensifying** that frequency from an outside source -- his frequency ray tube -- he made the microbe shake until it disintegrated or gathered into a devitalized clump. Then the immune system could remove the dead trash and the body healed after a series of treatments. The dynamic instigator or at least an accompanying element of cancer was **painlessly eliminated**.

This successful process was validated in the laboratory with albino rats. It was validated in a clinical trial with patients who were in a "terminal" condition. It was validated by medical doctors who cured cancer patients in their offices by having operators run the devices for a few minutes with each patient. Up to 40 patients a day in one clinic were being treated and healed after a series of treatments lasting three months or so! "Resonant Frequency" therapy was indeed a revolutionary find.

Yet ths amazing breakthrough discovery and invention was all stopped by medical criminals in order to prevent a new technology from competing with their traditional, unsuccessful treatments. Countless millions died because the medical authorities, defenders of orthodox treatments, in an unholy alliance with financial and political interests, opposed the further study and technological development of Dr. Rife's scientific discoveries.

Yet the government's upper management in its cancer institutions -- supposedly working for the common good and public health -- continued to support the false policy that Rife's claims were erroneus and impossible. They had to follow orders. A public admission that Rife's discoveries did work represented the experts' worst nightmare -- exposure of the wicked suppression, censorship and cover-up of Dr. Rife's historic contribution to medicine and microbiology.

Where are the gutsy investigative reporters and editors of the news "profession" who dare report this evil and corrupt situation? Where are the elected members of the U.S. Congress who will demand hearings to determine the ugly truth and put it on the record?

The cancer industry experts filled their own pockets while countless patients died because the cancer industry's most prestigious members refused to honestly examine Rife's discoveries and the documented facts of its scientific value. An entire microbiology frontier was kept hidden from objective scientific evaluation because of medical politics.

The entire field of treating cancer by **resonant frequency disruption** of the disease's microbe cause has been ignorantly discarded by the elite cancer "authorities" and the politically appointed administrators of the nation's cancer "programs" -- all devoted to big profits and a cure "just around the corner." It's mostly a fraud. They never even allowed any real testing of natural therapies for healing cancer. The commitment was just to big profit methods -- chemo, radiology, surgery, gene manipulation and immunotherapy. Big ticket items for the experts of the cancer "industry."

No scientific fair play when the subject is Rife's super medicine so long suppressed by his scientific inferiors. Are ossified bureaucrats and political appointees chosen by powerful special interests running and ruining the official cancer programs and research choices for all Americans?

Test **resonant frequeny disruption** of the virus-sized microbe that causes or at least accompanies cancer in both laboratory samples and in clinical trials. Test the theory in practical, objective ways. Consider it as a breakthrough method to actually cure cancer. Which it once did!

Dr. Royal Rife could turn out to be one of the greatest American scientists to have ever lived.

But science scholars and news people were too scared to put scientific truth above their own comfort. It was too big a risk to publish anything objective and fair about the stunning "findings of Mr. Rife." So the truth about the phenomenal healing potential of "Resonant Frequency" therapy remained **off limits** for most serious scientists and investigators on the knowledge frontier.

All the evidence which indicated Rife had actually been a scientific master of the highest kind was kept out of mainstream publications and televised discussion. There were "special interests" who would be unhappy about any public disrespect for the "do not cross" line. The edict was clear: the Rife subject would remain essentially unexamined. The verdict against Rife would remain enforced.

So scientific scholars and science reporters chose not to probe very far into that forbidden subject. The gatekeepers kept the curious stopped at the border.

Did any prominent worthies have the gumption to open the Roy Rife issue straight up and wide? There is heavy gravity pulling this down where the darkness will keep it hidden. "Establishment interests" keep almost everyone totally misinformed. But Rife's scientific certainty about his microbes radiated like the Sun. He made them glow -- literally. And then he blew them up with a precise mortal oscillatory rate (MOR). **And changed the worlds of medicine and science forever.** No matter how long before he gains an historic recogniton for what he did!

"The device is a frequency generator that covers an extremely broad band. The machine oscilates on a frequency that coordinates with a resonant frequency of the chemical constituents of the micro-organism treated. When the coordinative resonance is reached, the micro-organism is devitalized; this is said to be the Mortal Oscillatory Rate or, as we term it, the M.O.R." (Royal Rife)

"Rife thinks that the lethal frequencies for various disease organisms are ... coordinates of frequencies existing in the organisms themselves ... Brief exposure to the frequencies ... brings the fatal reactions. In some organisms, it happens in seconds ... Now ... the ray can be turned upon that organism with the assurance that the organism will be killed." (San Diego Evening Tribune newspaper, May 6, 1938)

"For seventeen years Mr. Rife has succeeded in finding a vibratory rate which will kill the different invading organisms of the body. Having used this apparatus for almost two years, the writer has had the satisfaction of witnessing the disappearance of every malignant growth where the patient has remained under treatment." (Arthur Yale, M.D., California medical journal, 1940)

"With the frequency instrument treatment, no tissue is destroyed, no pain is felt, no noise is audible, and no sensation is noticed. A tube lights up and three minutes later the treatment is completed ... the body then recovers itself naturally from the toxic effect ... Several disease forms may be treated simultaneously." (Rife's 1954 report to the National Research Council which was rejected without examining the available evidence)

"We hope that by giving exposure to the original work of Rife it will encourage a more open-minded approach by those in the medical profession and thus further research and development in this important area ... Unfortunately for too long powerful organizations with vested interests have suppressed development and research in this area." (Editorial, Everyday Practical Electronics magazine, 2000 Great Britain)

"Disease organisms such as those of tuberculosis, cancer, sarcoma, typhoid and others may be observed to succumb when exposed to certain lethal frequencies peculiar to each organism, and directed upon them by rays." (Smithsonian Institution Annual Report 1944)

The cover-up was deep and wide. The cover-up and the denial of this phenomenon of **nature** that could have eliminated cancer more than 70 years ago.

Rife was very pragmatic. He built his instruments with extraordinary attention to detail. He was equally a perfectionist with his microbes in his laboratory. And he had a kind of genius "sonar" to find what he sought. He did find a new therapy for eliminating a number of human diseases. Yet the cancer experts refused to examine, openly discuss or independently test his original discoveries. He was not a member of their insider's club. He was an outsider. So they denounced him and killed any chance of his therapy being "authorized." This is called a tyranny of experts. A proven cure for cancer was suppressed.

Had the government's cancer authorities used their powers in a responsible way? The evidence is overwhelming that they sacrificed the public interest in order to serve orthodox medicine. Turning their backs on many viable "alternative" therapies.

The moguls wanted the profits that chemo produced. The government's cancer managers, directors and elite specialists got their marching orders. Cancer patients were denied any legitimate path to natural remedies. The public health interest lost to big dollar price gauging as the drug monopoly stayed in charge as the priority treatment for cancer.

The people of America are not dumb. Many concluded a long time ago that their nation's cancer programs were rigged to benefit the moguls and the pharmaceutical cartels. And the oncologists who specialized in drugs.

The "credentialed" cancer scientists wouldn't even look for the cancer-causing micro-organism that Rife had finally isolated. They knew better. Scientists who went against the ruling dogma were ostracized.

It was a terrible crime that the "professional class" in charge of the cancer industry had condemned the scientific findings of Dr. Rife. The rejection of a true scientific breakthrough was all political, exacerbated by criminal intimidation and the bribing of doctors and scientists who were silenced. Millions of cancer patients were denied a therapy that did cure their disease. A monstrous massacre occurred because businessmen and bankers were determined to get big payoffs from toxic drugs hyped as magical potions. Alternative methods were forbidden to be developed. This evil collusion will be recognized by future historians. Those who participated will have legacies of shame. The public health was sold out.

Rife's therapy needs to be revived. He found something in nature that is eternal. A lot of cancer patients will be cured. And even more people will have cancer prevented.

The Cover-Up Of "Resonant Frequency" Therapy For Cancer

The Cover-Up Of "Resonant Frequency" Therapy For Cancer

What Have The Cancer Oligarchs Done?

It is extraordinary how the cancer authorities of the U. S. government, along with the big private cancer institutions with all their esteemed "leaders in the field" have managed to keep in place a rigid trade barrier against viable alternative therapies that have cured cancer in both clinical trials and individual doctors' office settings. There is an obvious anti-trust issues here that should be recognized as an impediment to finding a genuine, lasting cure. Something better could be put in place if entrenched interests were exposed and if separate, competitive disciplines were given strong legal protection. It's a very lucrative racket that currently exists because of how the nation's "cancer programs" are controlled and how alternative therapies are restricted. Both by law and by research priorities that favor insiders.

But a reform of the grotesque injustice that now exists throughout the established cancer system is unlikely to happen soon. Why? Because the cancer system is rigged to serve the professionals and the providers, with treatment choices restricted by powerful financial and political forces. The money flows to a cancer research world clearly separated from significant public input and distorted by a dependence on those with "credentials and connections." It's a club for insiders protected by law and the myth that unaccountable specialists should have life and death power over the final "authorization" of any cancer treatment. That's a barrier put in place long ago which guarantees that orthodox medicine appointees remain in charge of "standard practice" guidelines. It also keeps the market closed to any competition from new technlogies or innovative approaches. Anything truly original must undergo a brutal, expensive, rigorous ordeal that wears out who or what dares intrude on the cancer club's private domain. The result? **Many viable treatments for cancer are prohibited from being used, tested and further developed.**

"Resonant Frequency" therapy is one alternative method that deserves a thorough testing. But it won't get any serious attention because this therapy threatens established interests. Thus, even though it should be a priority subject for well-funded research and experimental development, followed by clinical trials, it won't be! The last thing that the "leaders in the field" will permit is a comprehensive study of the "Resonant Frequency" science. A dozen or so qualified clinics flush with sufficient money to carry out independent, competitive examinations of this bioelectric field might bring stunning progress in treating cancer.

Why won't they? After all, the cancer establishment is supposed to be guided by science-based medicine developed through credible research of different fields in order to find a lasting solution to cancer. Right? Well, that kind of thinking is fine and good when applied to treatments that are familiar to the experts -- comfortable areas where they have knowledge. It's also why the orthodox cancer industry has continued to thrive for so many decades despite its meager results. They instinctively obstruct innovation approches because it is a threat to their positions and their specialties. Virginia Tech science professor Henry Bauer explained that:

there exist knowledge monopolies composed of international and national bureaucracies ... these monopolies at the same time are research cartels ... Instead of disinterested peer review, mainstream insiders insist on their point of view in order to perpetuate their prestige and privileged positions. (Henry H. Bauer, Journal of Science Exploration, Vol. 18: Science in the 21st Century.)

Thus, when a truly new and even radical procedure appears that is outside the familiar range of medical knowledge and scientific acceptance, then the response has been and will likely remain one of open opposition. If any new innovation could upset the high incomes and the elevated postions of the established authorities in the cancer world, then it will be ignored, lost or openly attacked. Whatever the cost in lives might be and whatever the new knowledge might deliver for the future well-being of the entire society. If it is a threat to the bosses and their interests, it will be fought ferociously with every underhanded and even criminal method imaginable. As will be described later. That's why the corrupt structure of the existing "cancer industrial complex" needs to be fundamentally changed. Or a separate, competitve structure created. The public interest requires that the current corruption and injustice be openly, publicly examined and transformed. Who decreed there should be a monolithic approach to treating cancer?

Any move toward open testing and experimenting with "Resonant Frequency" therapy could uproot what is essentially a feudal oligarchy characterized by deliberate obstruction of anything that competes with the profitable status quo. "Resonant Frequency" therapy was outlawed by arbitrary fiat, not by fair, independent tests that produced negative results. Objective evaluation hasn't ever been allowed with this cancer treatment. The insiders have too much to lose. This therapy is a totally original way to treat cancer that was forbidden because it came from an outsider with superb scientific credentials.

The cancer authorities have the money. They have the power. They have the press complacent and obediant to the pronouncements from the top. It's a hierarchy that resembles a ruling class. They are interconnected by conferences, peer-reviewed journals, and government agencies using the law and regulations to punish those who dissent.

They share a worldview with others in their profession who are similarly educated and who have common experience with the same medical tools. They have been similarly indoctrinated. And they are the authorities who set the agenda. And no Galileo-like maverick is going to introduce radical medical ideas into their exclusive domain! Honest testing of alternative methods is simply not done.

The cancer bosses owned the authorization procedures, the cancer testing network, the cancer research worlds, and the entire structure that determined how anything in the cancer industry gained financing, traction and eventual acceptance. And Congress failed to perform its watchdog function. Thus, "Resonant Frequency" therapy was quickly discredited for "political" reasons. It quickly went on a "taboo" list. But interest in the subject remains high. Here's why:

Many decades ago, a great scientist, inventor and microbiologist had one of the finest medical research laboratories in the world. In this place, surrounded by some of the most advanced equipment of his time, much of which he designed and built himself, he conducted a series of ground-breaking experiments with micro-organisms.

In the process, he found the microbial causes of many deadly diseases. And then, continuing to probe into the unknown, he also discovered that these organims could be consistently destroyed by a then unknown, but unique and non-invasive method. He safely obliterated the pathogens by using their own natural "Resonant Frequency" against them. By just intensifying that frequency through an outside source, the dangerous microbes would shake until they burst!

Voila! A new way to cure diseases and heal patients without damaging any other cells, tissues or organs. A scientific breakthrough of the first order. Just as powerful as anti-biotics and certainly safer.

These living organisms of virus-size were filtered from larger bacteria using various chemical concoctions or what are known as "cultures." This process caused the release of smaller, deadly, virus-sized "particles" from the larger organism. The resulting particles or "filtered forms" were the long-sought cause of many deadly diseases, including cancer. This scientist was the first person to ever isolate them and categorize them into separate "tables" or convertible groups of deadly, **living**, virus-sized organisms. Each linked to a specific disease. By color and by frequency!

Among his findigs were the causes of cancer, tuberculosis, typhoid and 40 or more other disease-causing microorganisms. He had all their own "Resonant Frequencies" identified along with the different forms into which they could mutate. Cancer had a fungus form as well as a virus form, depending on the culture in which it lived. This was corroborated with a nationally known cancer expert when they observed the effects of different cultures on the same entity.

So, by **feeding back** the germ's own natural "Resonant Frequency" from an outside source, he could obliterate it. The deadly "filtered forms" would shake intensely and then burst or gather into a devitalized clump that could no longer infect lab animals. No drugs were needed to reverse the disease and restore a healthy metabolism through other means. The causative agent had been eliminated.

The method was tested under the microscope. The method was tested with cancerous albino rats. The method was tested on terminally ill cancer patients. It worked over and over again and it healed all patients in a cancer clinical trial guided by a group of nationally prominent doctors and scientists!

Today, in modern, 21st century times, many decades after the scientist made the original discovery, physicists and engineers are resurrecting this scientist's great work. His original instruments have been found and reverse-engineered. New devices have been designed in more efficient or simplified versions. The successful research from decades ago has been revived! Experiments are on-going.

II

Unfortunately, the "leaders in the cancer field" -- the established authorities -- are adamantly opposed to this and other methods that challenge their monopoly on cancer therapies. It threatens to wipe out all their expensive, failed remedies that in effect are forced on the public as the only therapies allowed to be used by doctors in "treating" cancer patients. This is a classic case of protecting a monopoly interest. A viable cure is kept illegal so that "organized" medicine and corporate interests -- big drugs, big professions, big hospitals -- can maintain their exclusive license, their financial power, their status, and their prestigious expertise by suppressing competition. Only in this case, it is human lives that are sacrificed in order to protect entrenched products and services.

Established cancer authorities have no understanding of and no interest in "Resonant Frequency" therapy. So they adamantly oppose any honest investigation and open testing. The "RF" therapy represents an industry-wide threat that could obliterate numerous cancer-related specialties along with overpriced products.

Thus the <u>commercial</u> barriers to "Resonant Frequency" therapy remain raised. It is absolutely no different than what China's government does to protect that nation's domestic businesses from foreign competition. The high-salared managers of the government's cancer organizations and departments and institutitons and agencies are protecting their own interests. The greater good and the public interest are ignored.

It is a monstrous wrong that this barrier prevents many patients from receiving the benefits of an inexpensive treatment which was known to work before criminal interests suppressed further development of the science.

The price that has been paid to protect the existing cancer fiefdoms is too costly -- the lives of innocent people and potentially greatly enhanced health for everyone. Denying access to this therapy and technology cannot be justified, as it currently is, by clever critiques from "leaders in the field."

The fix on this one is wide and deep, with almost everyone in the advocacy world, be it media, politicians and legal commentators avoiding the obvious rot and corrupt practices of the existing medical structure.

These monopoly practices also go against anti-trust laws that have been in place for more than a century. American laws enacted to insure that competition in markets would spur innovation.

So let's start with the hypothesis that real, profoundly disrupting and innovative therapies in cancer treatment are blocked by government experts and upper management who operate for special interests within the "medical monopoly." That is where both moral and commercial lines are crossed and where a pushback from an outraged public could quickly bring needed change.

Established laws and precedents permit the breaking up of concentrated industries. And if any industry is controlled to the point of being a clear danger to the ordinary citizen's health, it is certainly the cancer industrial complex.

Which delivers horrible, overpriced "remedies" that damage the patient's health. While simultaneously restricting better alternatives, all because of domiance by a cancer oligarchy. The credentialed experts who are in control of the "approval process" keep out innovation. That's where the fundamental flaw in the system exposes it to pervasive corruption. The market is closed.

Breaking up monopolies goes to the core of America's commerical law. The first Supreme Court ruling against monopoly came in the early 1800s with the "Steamboat" case. (Gibbons v. Ogden.) Someone should remind Congress. Congressional probes could start the overhaul as expert after expert was ordered to come before a committee of Congress and to testify under oath why they are opposed to honest testing of this remarkable discovery and potential new science. Their opposition would wilt under such an examination. It would be a show for the ages.

This monopoly is maintained by government policy makers, allowing a terrible scientific and health injustice to endure. Everyone, including the supposed "Watchdog" press, ignores the problem because powerful interests benefit from the drug emphasis in the existing cancer industry.

It's such an overt racket and "conflict of interest." Here's an expert on the subject who was a witness to how drug company executives were sitting on the board of director at one of the nation's leading cancer centers and setting policy!

Ralph Moss is, perhaps the best medical journalist in the United States today. His book The Cancer Industry unconvered the corruption of the second most profitable business in the twentieth century -- cancer.

In an interview ... Moss elaborated ... "what happens, in effect, is that you have a closed circle of persons who are, on the one hand, directors of the world's largest cancer center; on the other hand, they are either officials or directors of the very companies that are producing the drugs which are used and advanced by these centers." (Jonathan Eisen, "Suppressed Inventions and Other Discoveries," from Scribd websdite.)

Everyone with any insight knows that the "approval" process is where the rigging takes place. New technologies are kept out and not allowed to prove their quality in open market evaluation. Even if many cancer patients were ready to volunteer for the trials. Patients do not have freedom of choice if products and procedures are prevented from reaching them.

The cancer establishment does its decision-making behind closed doors and from corporate towers where pressures are applied, orders are sent out, and hidden factors influence final decisions. It's easy to buy medical committees that act as juries when this kind of medical structure has been in place for decades. The public becomes accostomed to slow, years-long "reviews." Why not just end it? Give patients legal access to experimental therapies. The world of "experts" in medical approvals and clinical trials has been shown to be corrupt, morally wrong and not reliable. It produces errors and abuse. Yet the illusion of its worth remains.

The rapid healing of many cancer patients might result if "Resonant Freqiemcy" instruments were allowed to be widely tested and compared. So that the quality designs could be identified and separated from the rip-off devices made by quick-buck con artists. Or deluded "garage engineers" who are unaware of the latest developments.

Unfortunately, the mainstream media has always been timid about in-depth investigation of the cancer establishment and reluctant to expose the many flaws, deceitful practices, and lack of oversight for what would most benefit the public. So the tale of a competitive new therapy with great potential, such as "Resonant Frequency" therapy stays censored by the mainstream press. This is self-imposed censorship by the news people. The press avoids the topic because it bows to pressure to "stay quiet" about this science-based method. The so-called "experts" are in charge of approving or forbidding a therapy that they do not understand. Does that make any sense? Should such a flawed system be allowed to continue? Of course not.

"Resonant Frequency" therapy was once going to be a major story on a national TV Network! Until pressure came from the network higher ups who feared losing drug advertisements from pharmaceutical giants made "unhappy" by the scheduled broadcast.

If the broadcast and print press started talking and writing about the scientific theories underlying the "Resonant Freqiemcy" cancer treatment, then curiosity in scientific circles could generate wide public interest. That's something the cancer elite would want to prevent. Keeping cancer studies plugged into the familiar channels is their primary goal. That's why "RF" therapy remains an off-limits topic for the press. A couple of odd-ball newspaper stories here and there certainly can be managed. But a full court press by countless newshounds supported by their institution's massive fact-checking apparatus? An entire industry could collapse in the ensuing scandal. The toxic "cancer industrial complex."

The money at stake is colossal. Even that word fails to provide a true picture of how much money could shift from failed products (overpriced chemo, for instance) and failed specialist fees to an entirely new start-up structure with cancer-causing microbes being periodically eliminated in a few treatments every couple of years at walk-in clinics. Goodbye cancer centers with their million dollar equipment being auctioned off at junkyard prices!

Just consider how miseducated and misinformed most microbiologists are about the world of pathogens discovered by the scientist who established a table of disease organisms identified solely by their own natural frequency. Just consider how medical diagnoses would be transformed once these minute "filtered forms" were spotted in blood tests and then zapped by the appropriate "Resonant Frequency?" Or consider how universities would have to hire entire new departments qualified to teach the new science and the new medicine.

So there's a potential medical revolution in the making. Once people are informed about what has been discovered and then suppressed, ending the cover-up of scientific truths unwanted by the "leaders in the field," then wholesale change will be inevitable. These truths about "Resonant Frequency" therapy would devastate the cancer industrial complex. With its huge monopoly profits. Which it intends to maintain despite their lousy results.

The scientist who discovered the "Resonant Frequency" method of treating disease conditions did what he claimed. Microphotos of these tiny organisms were published and can still be viewed on the internet! These microphotos were taken 3 decades before the electron microscope verified the ratios in the same organism! Tough to disparage evidence like that. It all appeared in an article published in a *Smithsonian Institute Annual Report* many decades ago. And it was totally ignored by the high paid government medical priesthood in charge of the nation's health! What a fumble on their part. Yes, they were incompetent and deserve the public's scorn. As do the current holders of those esteemed positions with their national responsibilities for protecting and improving the public health. Using the most efficient technology available. Well, they didn't. They failed to look.

Imagine. They are not interested in a scientific method that could reverse deadly diseases through a painless, non-invasive "frequency bath" lasting only a few minutes! As the successful cancer clinical trial and other clinical healings demonstrated.

Yet the established medical and science authorities proclaim that there's nothing to this "Resoant Frequency" stuff. They are either uninformed about a new science field that has enormous potential if development were encouraged or they're deliberately lying because that's what "the Old Guard" always does. The authorities and experts and managers putting forth the lie that "Resonant Frequency" therapy was disproved need to be challenged. Testifying under oath or being probed by pushy newshounds are all that is needed to bury the offical falsehood. The cancer elite have mislead the public for decades about the potential of this area, determined to stall long-overdue studies and clinical trials to verify this worthy field.

Instead of relying on ignorant experts putting out negative opinions, tests should be started to determine the truth or the falsity of this therapy. That's not difficult. It's a corrupt power structure that is the real obstacle.

The cancer authorities are protecting their own interests and stopping "Resonant Frequency" therapy because to test it would expose decades-long incompetence of those in charge of America's entire cancer program. How can they admit that they ignored and dismissed a science find of this magnitude throughout their careers? Why did this happen? Because they chose to play the political game instead of searching for scientific truth. Wherever it might be.

There is reason to mistrust the medical elites for keeping everyone very uninformed about their secret procedures and questionable allegiances. The safety and effectiveness of "Resonant Frequency" therapy could have been determined very fast if honest scientific testing had been permitted. A lot of cancer treatments favored by the upper management of the U.S. government's cancer institutions and by the executives of private cancer centers were just bad, misguided or hyped. (Consider the horrible "bone-marrow transplant" fiasco which made fortunes for hospitals, but brought immense pain and many deaths for its breast cancer victims!) If the "Resonant Frequency" therapy was recognized, huge sums of money spent on toxic chemo would soon evaporate. **Crisis would hit a corrupt cancer industry**.

"Resonant Frequency" therapy is a solid science that is being kept from objective evaluation by people who fear what the truth may be. Their interests lie elsewhere.

In the cancer world, the ruling elites have abused their powers and suppressed breakthroughs in areas outside their own knowledge bases. Authorities instinctively defend their own skills and methods, resisting the innovative until the new gains momentum. The defenders are so busy in dealing with their own priorities and those identified as hot by the "leaders in the field" -- immunotherapy and genetic signatures and on and on.

But "Resonant Frequency" therapy is an unusual, quality alternative, with conceptual elegance and substantial evidence that it was effective in healing people with serious disease conditions, even those who were diagnosed as being terminally ill.

Nevertheless, "Resonant Frequency" therapy is ignored and verbally trashed by the government's experts who failed to do their jobs by not allowing the therapy to be honestly studied. Their position is indefensible. The public interest and the cancer patients' interests were sacrificed because the government's cancer experts and institutional "upper management" were playing the career game and supporting standard procedures, which in general kept failing. Such stupidity. Such arrogance. Such failure to act for the public interest and the public health.

The managers and commissioners habitually duck, weave and stall when questioned about why "Resonant Frequency" therapy doesn't work. They have never tested it! Yet they are adamant that it is a worthless pursuit. The reasons they give for their animosity are simply deceptive excuses. No straight answers from "official medicine" is ever forthcoming. Because they dare not admit, "We were never allowed to test it." Scientists and doctors get to a certain corporate or government institutitonal level and learn quickly to "play it safe." They follow the policy line of their company or agency. Here's how the system actually works:

The groups with the greatest stake ... elite scientists whose influence depends on satisfying their patrons ... A government or corporate researcher who releases findings or speaks out in any way critical of the organizational view -- or who makes any action that challenges the line of command -- is a prime target for attack. ("Science: Contemporary Censorship" by Brian Martin, from Censorship: World Encyclopedia, Vol 4)

The cancer authorities should be condemned for this charade. The subject of "Resonant Frequency" therapy deserves a serious scientific inquiry. With a first class team of investigators committed to truth and the public health.

What ever happened to the sacred "scientific method" that starts wih observation and experimental testing? This was never allowed for "Resonant Frequency" therapy. "Resonant Frequency" therapy has solid theoretical and practical reasons to be honestly tested. Period. So what is the real problem?

The history of cancer treatment in America is replete with suppression of worthy methods which deserved objective, independent evaluation. But instead, medical power prevailed and standard treatment methods were protected and imposed. Regardless of what the patient wanted. There was organized efforts to keep the medical treatment market closed to any real competition. The scheme worked. Cancer patients kept dying. While the outrageous price gauging continued.

For all intents and purposes, healthcare in America is now under the control of a vast and corrupt medical monopoly ... When multiple companies, very often competing companies work together to create a monopoly, we call it a cartel. These competing companies work in concert to eliminate the outside competition and thereby strengthen the cartel as a whole. (Dr. Brad Case, "Genesis of the Medical Monopoly")

The "Resonant Frequency" therapy was very successful in curing a significant number of cancer patients who had reached the terminally ill stage. For those patients, a stunning healing did take place!

Yet the government's cancer authorities and the private cancer cartels prevented this therapy from being studied and tested. Let alone further developed through serious funding and experimental evaluation of different instruments. What criteria were these cancer experts applying? They approved chemo that had abysmal cure rates but denounced a super breakthrough therapy that did cure cancer. See what powerful interests and their lobbyists have done to the scientific process? Why have these cancer officials never been asked to account for this betrayal of the public's trust? Not just interrogation by members of Congressional Oversight Committees, but by newshounds from both print and television acting as representative voices for the public!

The agents of the American Medical Association (AMA) busted into the offices of doctors who were using "Resonant Frequency" instruments and confiscated the new technology. They wouldn't allow inexpensive devices to wipe out the skills and fees of traditional doctors. The AMA boss sent orders from its headquarters to grab the technology. No law existed that allowed such theft of a doctor's private property. The AMA's head guy imposed his own tyranny and greed on innocent patients who were benefiting from the new technology. All just to prevent competition from a better therapy than was then generally available. This is how special interests obstruct competition. It is illegal. A criminal interferred with medical progress.

No consideration was given to the success that the doctors were getting with the "Resonant Frequency" instruments. So the AMA just grabbed them and destroyed them. After this original suppression occurred, the U.S. government agencies such as FDA continued the policy. Suppression without any testing. With a message to the wise to stay clear of anything relaated to this original approach to healing cancer and other diseases. One businessman considered mass manufacturing the original instrument. He was paid a visit from the FDA and warned he had better not. This is such an outrageous abuse of power by a government agency that it crosses into the category of criminal behavior. Corruption of this kind obviously exposes something fundamentally criminal that is functioning within the government to protect private interests within the cancer industry.

The timid press never reported these nasty events or the pattern they represented of a medical tyranny that operated outside the law and was beyond practical protections of both citizen's rights and doctor's rights. A massive reform of the entire medical structure and its hierarchical rigidity is long overdue. The "experts" failed the public they were supposed to serve with their unique skills, instead taking orders from politically appointed managers attentive to their opportunities in post-government employment with private sector businesses needing "insider skills."

The government cancer officials have banned and bad-mouthed the "Resonant Frequency" therapy ever since the AMA and the drug companies opposed it. Independent evaluation of the new science was never allowed. The therapy was consistently denounced by ignorant opponents who used their positions to block its use. The interlocking interests of cancer experts and investment forces have many people ready to stop any public curiosity about this scientific and commercial matter. Lots of $ on the line!

Still, sometimes the "vested interests" blunder and something telling slips out and gets the public's attention. That's how many revolutions are triggered. People get offended by what is being secretly done to them by powerful forces in back rooms! Or through connections and networks. And eventually enough people start to protest and force deep change in a very corrupt system. Sometimes a big industry is even transformed into what is now called a more "transparent" operation. With the press attentive to the reforms and suspicious of the old guard's maneuvers to keep things in their favor.

It is important to remember history. The chiropractors had to prove in court that the AMA was involved in a conspiracy to prevent that healing technique from being practiced. The court ordered the AMA in 1987 to stop or there would be consequences. The AMA now pretends to leave the chiropractors alone in a separate place of their own. Something similar may be needed for practitioners of alternative therapies in the future. Such as those who operate "Resonant Frequency" instruments. The Law of the Land declaring that competition in medicine is protected and that citizens have the absolute right to use alternative therapies and to have access to innovative technologies. Thereby legally prohibiting interference from the medical monopoly and drug cartels.

III

The "Resonant Frequency" therapy did actually cure patients who were in a terminally-ill, stage 4 condition. All cancer clinical trial participants were diagnosed as "clinically cured" by a group of highly qualified doctors who were observing the effects of the experimental devices. The first cancer clinical trial of the new therapy and new science resulted in a 100% success rate! Using only terminally-ill cancer and tuberculosis patinets in the trial.

Yet the cancer authorities won't honestly test this therapy? They let people suffer and die with the old "approved" methods, even if those preferential, expensive treatments don't work? This is immoral. It's not just incompetence on display, but an entire system that is absolutely indefensible, no matter how smoothly the excuses are presented in pleasant phrases from a white-haired member of the medical gentry.

The cancer bosses ordered that the radical therapy was not worthy of study and testing, regardless of its clinical success? They had all kinds of interesting, well-financed programs being run by armies of credentialed superstars and "traditional" researchers with political clout. Some of these "leaders in the field"were "pulling down" more than $300,000 a year in comfortable academic chairs and passing on their traditional views to those who would rule the cancer world for decades to come. Carrying on the standard ignorance and prejudices. This system needs fundamental disruption. Here's a pertinent explanation of how the medical world really works and why it needs fixing:

No one knows the total amount provided by drug companies to physicians, but I estimate from the annual reports of the top nine US drug companies that it comes to tens of billions of dollars a year ... Its extensive ties to ... senior faculty at prestigious medical schools affect the results of research, the way medicine is practiced, and even the definition of what constitutes a disease. (Marcia Angell, former editor of the prestigious New England Journal of Medicine, from an article titled "Drug Companies and Corruption," The New York Review of Books, January 15, 2001.)

So the "Resonant Frequency" therapy was forgotten or "lost" in the shuffle of time and cancer industry priorities. High-priced priorities. The mantra is familiar in this world when "Resonant Frequency" therapy is occasionally discussed. It goes like this, "Oh yeah, I heard something about that, but I was busy and didn't really look into it. Kind of far-out stuff, I recall. Controversial. It might harm a career to go there. And competition for the grants is tough. Best to keep my nose clean for now."

"Resonant Frequency" therapy was officially declared to be "not efficacious" by a panel of elite scientists associated with the National Academy of Sciences. They came to a philosophical conclusion against the totally unknown but successful method for treating cancer patients. They didn't bother to look at the evidence. They chose not to communicate with the pioneering scientist. They didn't interview the witnesses, nor the supporting scientists, nor the doctors involved. And they were't interested in watching a demonstration of a previously unseen microorganism of virus-size be blown up by intensifying its own unique natural "resonant frequency." After all, nobody in the science world in which they were preeminent were doing anything like that!!!! Had to be impossible. Some crackpot. Best to ignore that therapy and concentrate on the new chemo that regular oncologists were testing. Much safer political position also.

The dignatories who hold high honors for past accomplishments do not like to see the current progress rush past them. (German biologist Hans Zimmer, quoted in "Does Medicine Have a Bad Attitude?" by James P. Carter.)

Remember, these were the best scientists in the entire cancer field. They knew everything that was important. And also what was politically dangerous.

How does one defend such arrogance, incompetence or corruption? Serious science referees or judges who take on such an analysis of a potential leap in knowledge and medical treatment do have obligations to honor strict standards and to deliberate in good conscience. Yet these mandarins showed no curiosity about what they didn't understand? These are indefensible actions for the "leaders in the field." Who serves the public interest in this kind of examination of a fundamental science issue? The public interest is, after all, the basis of any law. The impartiality and supposed superiority of these judges was a joke.

Should the senior management of the government's cancer institutions be regularly grilled to determine if they have closed off all channels for scientific progress that are not a product of the credentialed class or the peer-reviewed journals? Limiting projects to a privileged caste of cancer "aristocrats" with the right kind of resumes or "pedigrees" suggests something alien to American values. Sure seems like something's amiss in the very structure and procedures by which new cancer therapies are funded and "scientifically" examined.

Could it be that the cancer hotshots ignored or obstructed what might become the premium cancer therapy of the future? Eliminating cancer at the virus level? Could those who ran the cancer organizations for decades have been adherents of the anti-microbe school that dominated the cancer establishment for many generations? Those elites rejected projects that had a microbial element at its core. Was this the taboo that "Resonant Frequency" therapy dared to challenge? Therefore bringing an immediate condemnation and rejection?

At best, the government cancer managers were incompetent or afraid to challenge powerful "interests" within the cancer industry. Where politics is known to operate, according to experienced whistleblowers. At worst, the cancer authorities were paid or pressured to lock out anything which might replace the oh-so-lucrative chemotherapy priority. Maybe the operational managers who were selected to run the entire nation's cancer programs were chosen by their preference for drug therapies, committed to bury any alternative methods that competed with the payoffs from the **golden goose** provided by Big Pharma. Maybe Big Money would be watching to see what was emphasized and what was firmly discouraged.

The professional "leaders in the field" of cancer need to be consistently interrogated harshly by Congress and its professional investigators. The press needs to become involved also. Especially the science journalists who can watch how government grants tend to be narrowly focused. The government's cancer management have too much life-and-death power to be allowed to rule from out-of-touch sanctuaries. With their concentrated power to promote or discourage any unique alternative which might redirect the priorities of the nation's entire cancer program. Here's why:

In 2004, Fortune magazine published an investigative report on cancer. It was written by the magazine's executive editor. After interviewing numerous top scientists, physicians, government officials, drug executives and patients, he concluded that the very structure of the cancer research system was fundamentally flawed. Grants were going to researchers who were focused on "incremental improvements," using safe, well-known models. Big, daring, "new approaches" weren't funded.

After more than 30 years of massive investment in the "War on Cancer" (1971-2004), it apparently was obvious to everyone that the strategy made no sense and that the program was mismanaged. The professionals had learned a lot, but there was very little progress towards finding a cure. Yet, despite the exposure, the government's cancer program was not radically altered. It went on as before.

People in both public and private institutions, persuing careers in the field were trapped in rigid procedures and groupthink, leading to mountains of publications and academic prestige, but producing few breakthrough approaches.

Does that surprise anyone? Natural therapies were never tested. They were ignored and aggressively suppressed while the cash went to career scientists attending lots of conventions and producing articles for "hundreds of journals over the years." While therapies that had cured cancer -- also not searched out by the Fortune investigator -- were condemned because their methods were "theoretically" impossible. Even if they worked!

What can be more decadent than government "managers" strangling viable cancer therapies while disgorging billions of dollars to research the established and favored areas of inquiry?

... virtually all of these experts offered testimony that, when taken together, describes ... a dysfunctional "cancer culture" ...

Indeed, the cancer community has published an extraordinary 150,855 experimental studies on mice, according to a search of the PubMed database. Guess how many have led to treatments for cancer? Very, very few. In fact, if you want to understand where the War on Cancer has gone wrong, the mouse is a pretty good place to start. ("Why We're Losing The War On Cancer," by Clifton Leaf, with Doris Burke, Fortune magazine, March 22, 2004.)

In other words, the money was misspent.

IV

What follows is a segment from an old newspaper article about the science of "Resonant Frequency." Before the heavy suppression and censorship became organized. The newspaper story was from many decades ago and stirred both intense public interest and a furious backlash from entrenched "interests." The article was published at the time "Resonant Frequency" instruments were healing a lot of people with various diseases, including cancer. Is this a good candidate for a "cold case" review and maybe some serious cancer research funding? You bet it is. Thousands of private eye scientists, engineers, doctors and patients should pursue it. And maybe even a couple of those tough old news hounds or tough younger generation news hounds.

The suppression came fast after this news article appeared. There were bribes and threats put on scientists and doctors who were witnesses to the therapy's success or who were experimenting with and studying the microbial world that had been opened for the first time by making these tiny "filtered forms" glow by coordinating their light frequencies through microscope viewing.

Suddenly, scientists "lost interest" or received big grants to study some other area. A lot of pressure was applied to stop the therapy from taking off. Doctors' offices were raided and "Resonant Frequency" instruments that were treating up to <u>40 patients a day</u> were confiscated by a crew of "guardians" from the medical society. The combination of gifts and attacks surely seems suspicious because they came so close to the newspaper article about the amazing possibilities of this new science and therapy. Followed by decades of refusal to study the evidence, the facts, and modern test results!

The dark forces succeeded. "Resonant Frequency" therapy was stopped cold. And when it emerged again briefly <u>15 years later</u> in a last, desperate endeavor to gain legitimacy and credibility from the government's cancer institutions or the National Academy of Sciences, its opponents moved quickly again to insure no actual investigation with consideration of the <u>evidence</u> or any <u>demonstration</u> ever took place.

An excerpt from the revealing newspaper explanation of the new science that had been experimentally proven:

... the lethal frequencies for various disease organisms ... are coordinates of frequencies existing in the organisms themselves. When the ray is directed upon them, they are seen to behave very curiously; some kind do literally disintegrate, and others writhe as if in agony and finally gather together in deadly unmoving clusters.

Brief exposure to the tuned frequencies ... brings the fatal reactions. In some organisms, it happens in seconds.

After the organisms have been bombarded, the laboratory reports show, they are dead. They have become devitalized -- no longer exhibit life, do not propogate their kind and produce no diseases when introduced into bodies of experimental animals.

... oscillatory rates for many, many organisms have been found and recorded and the ray can be tuned to a germ's recorded frequency and turned upon that organism with the assurance that the organism will be killed.

V

Despite careful laboratory research that determined the oscillatory frequency of dangerous pathogens and then many experiments in vibrationally "shaking" the disease-causing organisms until they broke up, thus beginning the reversal of that particular disease, the therapy remains an orphan. It's a rather simple concept or theory for a new science and potentially a major advance in the healing arts. Too bad the "experts" won't allow any clinical testing.

The elite cancer "professionals" and "managers" decided the method could not "theoretically" work. But theory is supposed to be only one starting point of a scientific pursuit. Practical results or their absence are determined by testing and experimentation. Yet the experts warn, do not test "Resonant Frequency" therapy. It might work.

The nation's top managers of all the cancer programs ignored the evidence supporting an alternative therapy that was outside their area of interest and experience. Even though the therapy had a solid record of success upon which to build new experimental models. The experts were snooty and privileged and not curious and unwilling to take a chance. It would cost only a little money and a few scientists who had reputations for integrity.

But big profits could be put at risk. Tens of millions of dollars annually could disappear forever if anyone in the cancer establishment had dared to demonstrate a bit of scientific integrity and a commitment to the public good. Instead, special interests that operate quietly and out-of-sight move the entire cancer research and testing programs in the way that they want. After all, money is tight. There's very little available for any new studies of "Resonant Frequency" therapy. The National Institutes of Health have a very small budget for the fiscal year 2017. **Only $33 billion**. And you wonder why the government researchers are fat, happy and complacent?

The powers-that-be kept chemo therapy unchallenged from frequency therapy. The cancer judges voted to continue the status quo. Here's why. It's an old practice for beating a competitor. Use the whispering game!

The new therapy must be disbelieved, denied, discouraged and disallowed at all costs, regardless of actual testing results, and preferably without any testing at all! (quoting medical investigative journalists Robert Houston and Gary Null, from "Cancer Reasearch -- A Super Fraud?" by Robert Ryan.)

Which goes against everything America, freedom of choice, and objective science is supposed to be about. Protected by law and vigorous oversight from Congress and a snoopy press. But the big owners of the cancer industry don't pay attention to the rules ordinary people must obey. Or what the public would expect its government "civil servants" to be on alert to find and to give a fair evaluation. Nope, doesn't work that way. Then what are they being paid to do? Maybe that should be spelled out.

To this day workable, testable alternatives to corporate medicine are not recognized by a system that is geared to maximize the profits of a pharmaceutical establishment. (Jonathan Eisen, "Suppressed Inventions and Other Discoveries," from Scribd website.)

Maybe the government's cancer elite should be ordered by elected members of Congress to stand down. Then Congress can initiate tests by capable, recognized researchers with reputations for independence and fairness to conduct an open test of "Resonant Frequency" therapy for cancer. With volunteers. That could bring an overnight crisis in the world of the cancer mandarins. For decades, they have prevented such tests from being done.

Suppose such tests proved to be a stunning demonstration of a "political tilt" in cancer research ever since the "War on Cancer" began gulping many, many billions of dollars from 1971 to the present time? A tilt to support expensive chemo and expensive other misguided notions that produced huge profits for the "politically connected." Suppose it all came under examination by top science historians? And the full, terrible racket was exposed for all to see? And then fixing it became a political imperative?

Remember what that newspaper reported long ago and which all the cancer experts, commissioners, directors and department cabinet members could never find because it didn't come from anyone in their insider's club that kept control of all cancer research, all cancer policies, and all cancer approvals. Here is another excerpt:

Discovery that disease organisms, including one occurring in deadly cancer, can be killed by bombarding them with radio waves tuned to a particular length for each kind of organism was claimed ... They are turned upon the organisms through a special directional antenna ...

So the great discovery was stopped from further development by the cancer establishment's massive opposition, supported by intimidation and bribes to turn scientists who knew about the discovery to cease any kind of complementary assistance. Or else. The helpers stopped helping. They went into a comfortable silence and abandonment of the genuine scientific breakthrough.

Science is not supposed to work that way.

Arrogant ignorance has followed science and medicine throughout history. (James P. Carter, "Does Medicine Have a Bad Attitude?")

Censorship of science ... affronts the fundamental premise of the scientific method. The purpose of science is to produce knowledge. If science is corrupted, what flows from it is not knowledge, but something else -- disinformation, propaganda. ("Joint Statement on Censorship and Science: A Threat to Science, the Constitution, and Democracy," Adu.org)

VI

Science is supposed to seek truth through observation, experiment, and attention to results in order to learn. Always alert to testing theory against hard factual evidence. Always open to inquiry and objective, impartial analysis by other independent researchers. But never the overt, deliberate suppression of a new discovery in science in order to maintain orthodox beliefs. Or in order to benefit special interests that are protecting some profitable monopoly. That constitutes corrupt practices. That is scientific fraud. There is lots of it in medical research according to top investigators.

The managers of the nation's cancer institutions are supposed to insure the integrity of its research projects and the honesty of its investigations. That's a hard case to make given the evidence that shows the very opposite is practiced. Especially when alternative therapies are the issue, political muscle will often call the result, not honest evaluation.

... science is the study of testable, observable phenomenon ... any good scientist ... must stand by the results of unbiased evidence and experimentation. (Bill Allen, National Geographic magazine, March 1998, page 1.)

Were there any honorable cancer specialists and managers in the U. S.

government's "health" departments, institutions and agencies who spoke out for doing what was right regardless of the pressure to conform? Who advocated an honest evaluation of the evidence supporting even one test of "Resonant Frequency" therapy? Apparently there were no voices for truth. Instead, they considered their own career interests and ignorantly assumed they could judge this totally different approach without any kind of test, not even a review of the documentation! They just intuitively knew it was too simple a treatment method. Couldn't possibly work, they all agreed. That's not science. That's being agents serving special interests and existing monopolies.

The people in cancer management -- for the entire nation -- ignored the facts and the evidence. They chose to defend orthodox treatments even though the results were appalling. After all, cancer cells were the target of the cancer elite and almost all the research money went in that direction. Cancer microbes were a touchy area and best avoided if career ambitions were to be advanced.

What a monumental error in strategy to dismiss cancer microbes and then to refuse to investigate a new, safe, painless way to identify cancer microbes and then destroy them. Stupid people with tunnel vision sitting in high government positions do terrible damage that sometimes stays hidden for decades.

The government cancer experts blindly supported gruesome treatments that consistently failed. These were protected from competition by the insider's group that controlled the monopoly. Doctors were discouraged from using natural remedies even if the patient requested one. Peer group pressure at the state or local medical society kept everyone in line. Those entrenched interests gave the orders with an implied threat if one dared to disobey. In more than one case, doctors who used natural remedies such as herbs were jailed for five years. That's how lawless governments work. That's how the medical oligarchy did work and sometimes still does work in America!

The "civil servants" in charge of all the nation's cancer programs were classic examples of how scientists in a corrupt government institution or agency functioned. It was a monopoly in which requests to test alternative therapies were denied even if the experimental treatment had delivered quality results.

Because in the world of cancer elites, a record of success had no effect. Because it was a monopoly. A medical monopoly.

... the rigidity of orthodoxy ... refuses to test and to prove or disprove new theories ... too prejudiced to admit of the possibility of any advance. (The Lancet medical journal, March 23, 1889, page 587.)

Standard treatments were imposed on the whole society despite awful effects. Innocent patients were betrayed by the medical chiefs. Few who worked in the cancer institutions dared to cry, "Foul." The press remained mostly uninterested, unwilling to dissect the cancer industry in the way it gleefully took on less powerful interests.

The actions and non-actions of the cancer elite were predictable and shameful. They served the powers-that-be and their own ambitions, not the public interest.

The "Resonant Frequency" therapy should be thoroughly, honestly studied, researched, publicly discussed and tested in order that the truth about this marvelous "lost" technique, technology, science breakthrough and forbidden method to destroy pathogens safely, non-invasively and painlessly can be known by all cancer patients and people suffering from other diseases who might benefit from an experimental "frequency bath."

Lots of independent scientists should be scurrying to learn the basics in order to take this knowledge further. Experimenting is how a society can learn and evolve. Not by suppressing the unknown because it doesn't fit into an old scientific paradigm. Medical institutions and medical schools suffocate under medical dogma. Which is what America's cancer bosses have imposed for many decades. In Washington, in cancer hospitals and in universities where the public should expect some disinterested inquiry. But even these eminent academic sanctuaries apparently "know nothing" about the science underlying "Resonant Frequency" therapy. Or its awesome medical potential.

Someone could catch a Nobel Prize just for replicating the long lost work of the still unrecognized scientific genius who first pursued and found at least one way to cure some cancers and several other diseases.

Maybe even the press will someday find the nerve to conduct an honest investigation of this long-lost, forbidden subject and then report the stark truth to a significant portion of the public that is convinced there was both a suppression and a cover-up of a viable cure for cancer. With all the facts. All the scheming and deceit exposed. All the vested interests that colluded to stop the therapy cold through intimidation and bribes. Nothing very sophisticated, just straight out muscle.

For decades to come, the many cancer officials inside the government's cancer institutions never knew a thing about this extraordinary treatment. Didn't show the slightest interest even after magazine articles and books revealed the ugly facts. Sure seems strange. Unless the therapy was officially "off limits." Could it be that such things actually happen in official government agencies and bureaus? Could be a criminal act deserving indictment. Maybe there should be some interviews of those "in the know."

"Resonant Frequency" therapy may be the Cinderella hidden away in the back room of the National Cancer Institute, metaphorically relegated to scrubbing the floors. Maybe some member of Congress will get curious and demand answers from the government's "cancer authorities" as well as from the power players of the private cancer centers who charge so much for the latest wonder drug, but who remain opposed to any inexpensive therapies even if it would actually cure their patients' cancers.

VII

IBM corporation's president claimed that it's supercomputer named "Watson" has combined massive data on cancer that enables any cancer doctor (oncologist) to have instant access to quality information in the designing of appropriate protocals for any given patient. (Fareed Zakari interview, *CNN*, September 18, 2016.)

But "Watson" won't include the potential super cure -- "Resonant Frequency" therapy. Why? Because orthodox medicine has not allowed any open testing. Nor have the prominent science and medical journals ever included any articles about the therapy during modern times. (*Science* magazine used to report on filter-passing forms, but their interest faded when the medical politics shifted from open discussion to absolute censorship.)

The therapy that cured many cancer patients before it was suppressed stays "lost." This is what corrupt systems produce. Corrupt policies. The threat to the entire "cancer industrial complex" is blocked by official cancer institutions, both public and private. Those who control the diaglogue determine the direction of the entire cancer program for the nation. That's why the absence of a press that pushes for answers has such a devastating effect. The cancer bosses get a free ride. Nobody's watching. Only those practicing the orthodox and "approved" methods get any press attention. Bad for the reputation of a "vigorous" free press.

After all, the bright corporate types from IBM and other corporate giants just "go along," enthusiastic about how they can manage all that digital data and organize all those thousands and thousands of cancer reports from the best in the field.

Just don't let "Watson's superbrain near "Resonant Frequency" therapy! It's super analytical data-crunching digital brain might come to the wrong conclusion and ask its human techies, "Where are the missing studies?" Or "Why did this therapy disappear?" Or, horror of horrors, "Why did the National Academy of Sciences investigation committee denigrate a science without investigating, without interviewing the principal scientists, without watching a demonstration of the technology? "Watson" might complain that its computer logic was upset with its human subjects who were keeping secrets from its knowledge banks. "Watson" might even accuse human medical officials of being corrupt. And what about next generation "Watson II" superbrains going to do with that big empty no-no subject of "Resonant Frequency" science? The reader should not assume this is fiction. If Watson becomes familiar with the internet, it will find

"Resonant Frequency" therapy even if its minders from the Medical Monopoly don't want the subject evaluated with data-crunching curiosity.

In other words, the "Watson" machine might disgorge the answer that the government's "authorities" have been hiding for decades!

VIII

Someday, someone within established medicine will talk to the press. And all the decades of cover-ups will be exposed. "Resonant Frequency" therapy for cancer will be a new hot topic for study and experimenting. To the utter shock and disgust of the American people who learn about the long cover-up. And how fair tests of this unique way to treat cancer were blocked because orthodox "experts" chose to avoid what was "risky" for their careers.

Resonant Frequency therapy isn't some synthetic concoction made in some chemist's lab for a multi-million dollar Big Pharma pitch. It's a reality of SCIENCE. It is part of NATURE. Why not apply it to ending cancer if a vulnerable "filtered form" associated with cancer can be destroyed by simply magnifying the same frequency from an outside source?

Where is the public interest that should be the basis of laws, regulatory policies, scientific funding and institutional priorities? The public interest has been replaced by the career interests of the cancer mandarins. Who themselves are mostly supporting established cartels invested in big profit products such as immunotherapy and well-paid, institutionally-sponsored genetic manipulation. The government's officials won't look at evidence or even consider anything not sanctioned by the industry of experts who have "appropriate" credentials.

They definitely won't analyze an inexpensive, science-altering wonder like "Resonant Frequency" therapy which stunned prominent physicians and scientists when they watched it actually heal supposed "incurable" diseases.

When a big scientific discovery changes the accepted knowledge of a critical field, there are usually intense reactions from those in high position who are about to be displaced. Organized attacks are mounted.

"Resonant Frequency" therapy is a threat to the traditional treatments that have driven medical research since the "War on Cancer" began in 1971. "Resonant Frequency" therapy could devastate many fiefdoms throughout the cancer industrial complex. It requires only honest testing to have its value widely recognized.

Remember the warning about the "military industrial complex?" Well, there is a very real "cancer industrial complex" that deserves watching too.

Make the medical authorities answer the tough questions about "Resonant Frequency" therapy before permitting a dismissal from the "experts." Take into consideration that some cancer experts are always protecting their own territories and records. Few are working for the public good, open to truly revolutionary leaps that might eliminate their own "knowledge monopoly."

You only need a few test cases with good results and rigorous controls to initiate a massive shift in the treatment of cancer for everyone. Lots of "experts" will fight it.

IX

It's likely the authorities will try to stall objective scientific investigations. They have too much to lose. They come from a world of big egos and years of experience being the ones in charge, the experts with the answers. They don't like being perceived as ignorant about anything in their field. And there are "influences" which will pressure them to support the reliable, the old, the standard remedies. It's an old game and it has brought cancer patients <u>four and a half decades</u> of hellish, outrageously priced failures. (Remember "bone marrow transplants?) Ever since 1971 when the racket known as the "War on Cancer" began to drain the United States Treasury.

Why not give "Resonant Frequency" therapy a fair chance to show its scientific value the right way? With honest tests and in-depth studies of its essential elements. It's how revolutionary science is legitimized -- when the old method's protectors are removed from their bullying jobs and replaced by objective, dispassionate people who examine the evidence instead of hindering its study.

Due process is required in the legal world. But in the search for a cancer cure, that procedure is absent! Strange how those "leaders in the field" rationalize their protectionism. They assume they are right and everyone else is wrong. Especially the public. So they hold back approval of the "Resonant Frequency" therapy. Even if they don't know a thing about it.

What about the citizen's right to contract for healthcare treatments of their own choosing? If the cancer authorities are preventing the citizen's freedom of contract, they have abridged a fundamental constitutional right. As one savy advocate for healthcare reform explained:

... the freedom to contract -- the right of individuals to decide with whom and for what services they will dispose of their earnings -- is one of the fundamental rights of man. (Sue A. Blevins, "The Medical Monopoly: Protecting Consumers or Limiting Competition?")

It is certain that the experts have served the entrenched interests and their own career ambitions for many decades instead of emphasizing the public's optimum health. If they were wrong in ignoring and prohibiting "Resoant Frequency" therapy, the terrible price in suffering and lives will be their legacy. A very bad one.

America should start questioning the medical mandarins. There needs to be new legislation that insures basic citizen freedoms are not restricted by a tyranny of medical experts. The right to contract for services of a medical nature should be spelled out. No different than the Miranda Rights which the police must tell a suspect when an arrest is made. Informing people of their medical rights would also serve the society's greater good. A real democracy would insure that citizens of every class know their rights. So people understand that their choice of medical care <u>cannot be restricted</u>. Again, Sue

A. Blevins provides direction:

... true health care reform must involve ending the government-imposed medical monopoly and providing consumers with a full array of health care choices.

There are already state laws that could serve as models for a federal law protecting patients from entrenched medical monopolies.

Where's the greater good? Letting the cancer authorities impose chemo and deny viable natural treatments because the medical specialists have rigged the system to eliminate competition? Or instead insuring there is a legal mechanism that guarantees alternative therapies are available for those who want them? The answer is obvious in a nation built on freedoms, rights and choices.

X

Criminal conspiracies at the start of the "Resonant Frequency" therapy breakout prevented it from being further developed and widely used. That criminal suppression should not be forgotten. It serves as a lesson about how far repressive medical interests will go to maintain their lock on "approved" cancer methods. The opponents of "RF" therapy will subvert the good science that is its basis. If they can get away with their behind-the-scenes rackets, using bribes and intimidation, a great healing art from nature itself may be prohibited forever. "Resonant Frequency" therapy needs some legal safeguards if it to be further developed. There could be some stunning health advances associated with this basic science. One doctor who experimented with it in his clinic was stunned to learn he was curing dozens of people with cataracts, as he reported in a letter to a renowned eye doctor.

Would competition produce better products and services for cancer patients? Absolutely. It only has the "cancer industrial complex" and its protective government "experts" standing in the way. They protect no one except the mandarins themselves. Their high incomes require that they engage in long, drawn-out procedings to be sure that something new may be "allowed." The cancer patient remains trapped. Choice is denied if only an elite priesthood always has the last say. Human history has certainly seen enough of that fraud. This has nothing to do with training medical specialists. It has everything to do with preventing them from having excessive power to determine what people can do with their own bodies -- where the legal right has been absolutely established in favor of the individual patient by definitive Supreme Court rulings.

Another description of this long covered-up scientific and medical process for curing cancer may deepen the understanding of this field's great potential:

The same principle which made living microbes visible was also used to kill them: resonant frequency. When increasing the intensity of the frequency at which a microbe resonates at, its natural oscillation also increases, causing it to distort and disintegrate from structural stresses ...

... viruses and bacteria could be selectively destroyed because each oscillates at a frequency unique from any other microbe. Subjecting them to an intensified version of that resonant frequency destroys them without harming anything else. (Essence-of-life.com)

This was handed to the cancer experts on a silver platter many years ago, but the entrenched interests came in and killed its development by intimidating and bribing many of the scientists and doctors who were associated with the original research or the initial treatment of patients. Some doctors who were quite prominent quickly went silent.

So how about testing it after so many decades of suppression and censorship? Or do we just follow the credentialed "leaders in the field" like medieval serfs who never gained the right to vote and choose its own experts and officials who were to be given the powers to govern. The people who were elected to serve the general welfare. Or so the U. S. Constitution clearly states. Somehow the medical wizards never got that message!

XI

One of the most respected medical science researchers in the world is Dr. John Ioannidis (pronounced yo-NEE-dees). His in-depth study of research published by the most exalted journals in the world produced a shock.

In 2005, he unleashed two papers that challenged the foundation of medical research ... researchers were frequently manipulating data, chasing career-advancing findings rather than good science, and even using the peer reviewed process ... to suppress opposing views. ("Lies, Damned Lies and Medical Science" by David H. Freedman, The Atlantic, November 2010)

An editorial in BMJ journal in June 2014 admitted the problem within medicine was enormous and had to be addressed. BMJ journal was formerly known as the British Medical Journal and is one of the most prestigious medical journals in the world. Its ediorial held nothing back. Its title was "Corruption: Medicine's Dirty Open Secret." The ugly truth was out for both the profession of medicine and for the public to face frontally.

Good governance, transparency, and zero tolerance must form the basis of any anti-corruption strategy. Changes must be implemented in society at large for reform to be sustained. Better government requires rigorous legislation and functioning administrative mechanisms.

The state of medical science stinks. One outstanding American scientist went far beyond what the British journal bemoaned. Dr. David L. Lewis is an internationally recognized research microbiologist.

Dr. David Lewis, former EPA / CDC scientist, described the fall of so-called government agencies to abject cronyism and corruption, knowingly putting the lives of millions of Americans in jeopardy, in his book Science for Sale. During his career Dr. Lewis was employed by private corporations, universities, and government agencies. He discovered that all three institutions have been corrupted and have been producing the non-scientific results their funders pay them to produce. (The summary originated with AntiCorruption Society which is found at anticorruptionsociety.com.)

The complete title of the Dr. Lewis book is: Science for Sale: How the US Government Uses Powerful Corporations and Leading Universities to Support Government Policies, Silence Top Scientists, Jeopardize Our Health and Protect Corporate Profits.

When all the existing corruption is acknowledged, one question remains. Has the upper management at the National Cancer Institute (NCI) and the leading private cancer centers obstructed a viable cancer therapy because a cancer establishment has denounced it? The eminent Dr. John Ioannidi said "most of what doctors do has never been formally put to the test in credible studies." (The Atlantic, November 2010)

Given that reality, why should "Resonant Frequency" therapy be denied to anyone who wants it and why can't doctors who want to use it for their patients be denied that option because some faceless bureaucrats and medical officials are prohibiting its fair testing and honest study?

There are outrageous conflicts of interest and corrupt practices in the cancer approval or disapproval process. These have stopped some very good therapies from being available to patients. Who should have had access to them on at least an experimental basis without long, bureaucratic struggles to have what is a natural and legal right -- to determine what will be done with their own bodies.

The evidence that a cure for cancer was found and then suppressed by special interests is solid. Resurrecting that lost science and therapy of "Resonant Frequencies" needs to be pushed by the public. So that the Congress would legislate it in order to force the "health institutions" to quickly do a full, honest evaluation and open, clinical testing. And if the President vetoes the legislation, there should be a Congressional override, mandating the law for the sake of the public interest and the health of everyone far into future generations. It could lead to an historic medical achievement. Finally. Decades overdue.

XII

"Resonant Frequency" science and therapy did cure cancer and other diseases many decades ago. In the early 21st century, a video was made that showed audiences how this little-researched field of science was used to treat a variety of diseases. The video also depicted how this remarkable scientific discovery was stopped from further development by medical and government officials.

In January 2004 and November 2005, a reviewer in the Townsend Letter For Doctors journal published two reviews and praised the video for what it contributed to saving the historic discovery:

The documentation and engrossing presentation of this little-known story of 20th century medical research creates a mind-shifting experience for those of us indoctrinated with a conventional view of biology. (Jule Klotter, Townsend review, January 2004)

It's a depressing tale of greed, character flaws, and despicable misuse of power by the American Medical Association and FDA.

The Rise and Fall of a Scientific Genius *deserves to be widely viewed and distributed as a tribute to scientific discovery and the misuse of power.* (Jule Klotter, Townsend review, November 2005)

A key part of the video involved a professor of pathology who explained how a pioneering scientist built a remarkable microscope that was able to make possible the first sighting of a living, virus-sized "filtered form" that had been isolated from breast cancer. By being able to see this previously unknown microbe that was associated with human cancer, the pioneering scientist could begin to experiment with its natural resonant frequency. He eventually discovered how to destroy the deadly microbe -- simply by intensifying that frequency. This was the method later used in the successful cancer clinical trial.

There may be numerous discoveries that result from the work of this pioneering scientist who found that living, disease-causing organisms of virus-size were vulnerable to "Resonant Frequency" rays. And, critically, as that scientist said, "with no harm to normal tissues."

There is agreement among science, medicine and metaphysics that certain frequencies can repel disease, and certain frequencies can destroy disease. Herein lies the link between frequency (vibration) and health.

Vibrational medicine ... is based on the idea of resonant frequencies, similar to a tuned string on a musical instrument resonating with anything tuned to the same frequency ...Vibrational medicine is one of the most, if not the most, widely studied field of medicine today. There is now global interest and research in the clinical applications of Vibrational Medicine.
(Altered-States.net/Barry/newsletter463)

The scientist who isolated the virus-sized microorganism associated with cancer was named Royal Rife. Here is a quick introduction to the field of science that he opened wide:

Dr. Royal Rife ... was a great scientist who had the vision of inventing a frequency generator with the potential to heal all kinds of disease. His research helped him to discover that all microorganisms ... have their own resonance frequency.

Once Dr. Royal Rife was able to determine a microorganism's unique frequency signature, he then exposed it to certain frequencies and high intensity light pulses until he found the right frequencies that could destroy the microorganism ... His experiments showed that the combination of certain frequencies and light pulses could destroy microorganisms without harming healthy cells and tissues. With this knowledge, he realized that a well-built frequency healing machine could heal many illnesses, including cancer. (Pao Chang, Energy Fanatics.com, March 4, 2014, updated October 3, 2016)

Unfortunately, the people in charge of orthodox medicine regarded Rife's descoveries as a threat to their own interests and specialties. Thus, the new science and its revolutionary healing potential was suppressed. The cancer establishment restricted treatments of cancer to only drugs, radiology, and surgery. The consequences of "official medicine's" open, relentless attacks against all alternative therapies and especially Rife's breakthrough science were catastrophic. And dishonest. They prevented any serious, in-depth evaluation and testing of alternative medicines or technologies. The medical establishment's actions were primative and tribal, lacking any relation to modern, objective science. That truth needs to be recognized and the medical science system fixed. It isn't hard.

Of course, "scientific medicine" maintains the fiction that the most effective therapies will be found through their own standards, their kind of studies, experimentation at their academies, and shared knowledge through peer-reviewed journals. And therefore should be given special protection by the state. In other words, control by "credentialed, qualified and experienced" professionals. It's a clever "spin" used by a trade group to keep out competition and to stop any Medical Freedom rights from being established by comprehensive law.

Rife invested years of research in determining observable facts the medical establishment had no interest in hearing and even less in researching for themselves! ... the strong wills of those in power in the medical establishment controlled permissable treatment, funding, and even what could get published in medical journals. (therapywave.eu)

Rife's success with cancer was kept secret. The esteemed National Research Council refused to examine the evidence that his discovery worked in a cancer clinical trial. They refused to watch a demonstration or even look into his microscope and see the deadly microbe disintegrate when the "Resonant Frequency" method was used. They concluded that the revolutionary discovery was "theoretically" impossible. It was a perversion of scientific evaluation.

The "revolving door" between upper management positions at the US government's cancer institutions, the big drug companies, elite academic medical schools, and the private cancer centers guaranteed that the cancer industry would not be disrupted by an outside genius such as Royal Rife. The cancer "aristocracy" protected its own through the all-too-familiar method of "contacts, grants and credentials." That is how insider clubs keep innovative breakthroughs from gaining recognition and commercial development.

XIII

Professor Samuel Epstein, M.D., the world-renowned authority on the causes ... of cancer and critic of the U.S. cancer establishment ... has been named a 1998 winner of the Right Livelihood Award, also known as the "Alternative Nobel Prize." (Criminal Indifference of the FDA to Cancer Prevention, books.google 2013)

Epstein: *"The highly biased ACS witch-hunts against alternative practitioners are in striking contrast to its extravagant and uncritical endorsement of conventional toxic chemotherapy. This despite the absence of any objective evidence of improved survival rates in reduced mortality following chemotherapy for all but some relatively rare cancers."*

The cancer industry's favor of pharmaceutical products is evidenced, Epstein said, "by the fact that the U.S. Food and Drug Administration has approved approximately 40 patented drugs for cancer treatment, while it has yet to approve a single nonpatented alternative drug."

(Noev M. Amell, "Criminal Indifference to Cancer Prevention," Nutrition Digest, Vol 38, Number 2, June 14, 2011)

But the most shocking revelation from Epstein is in reference to the massive conflicts of interest in the cancer industry. ACS, NCI, the National Institutes of Health, and other organizations all have close ties to one another. And they all band together to work to preserve the focus on orthodox cancer treatment methodology and philosophy. "Dr. Samuel S. Epstein Tees Off on National Cancer Institute and American Cancer Society," Smash Your Cancer, June 22, 2011)

The global market for cancer drugs has hit $100 billion in annual sales, and *could reach $147 billion by 2018 according to a new report.* (Mathew Harper, Forbes magazine, May 5, 2015)

XIV

Royal Rife and the Cure For Cancer

Rife (1888-1971), a scientist who worked for Zeiss Optics ... wanted to view living organisms, so he set out to design an optical microscope that worked by using light, refraction, and resonant frequencies.

In the early 1930s, Rife completed his "universal microscope," a device .. that did not kill the organisms being studied. Able to magnify up to 60,000 times, Rife became the first person to study living viruses ... Rife was able to focus his lenses to view these very tiny, dangerous, living organisms.

The key here is that Rife knew the resonant frequency of the virus ... in question. The specific rate of vibration was charted and catalogued. Using a simple principle of physics, Rife understood that if he overloaded the cell with the same frequency, it would eventually disintegrate ...

... replicate Rife's work ... so that the resonant frequencies of various diseases could be catalogued and hopefully cured. The cost is minimal, the benefits to humankind -- incalculable.

(Mark Seifer, Ph.D., Transcending the Speed of Light: Consciousness, Quantum Physics, and the Fifth Dimension, pages 58-60, copyright 2008)

The scientists and doctors of tomorrow will revive Dr. Rife's momentous discoveries and inventions, carrying them into mainstream practice and international honor.

The scientists and doctors of yesterday suppressed Dr. Rife because his breakthrough discovery would have replaced their own conventional cancer treatments. A description of Dr. Rife's cure for cancer has been sitting in the National Library of Medicine since 1954! Totally ignored and avoided by the high salaried managers of the national cancer programs. The library is a building right next door to the National Cancer Institute on the NIH campus in Bethesda, Maryland just a subway stop or two from Washington, D. C. All the billions of dollars spent on research to find the cause of and the cure for cancer during the "War on Cancer" from 1971 to the present was wasted.

Rife's scientific discoveries were buried by medical politics. And the so-called "scientific community" never let out a peep of protest. Rife's genius must be resurrected. It could enhance human health enormously.

How do we fix the "tyranny of experts" protecting their own interests by dogmatically suppressing competitive theories and therapies? Science philosopher Paul Feyerabend recognized the problem and dramatized its danger to democratic societies:

Feyerabend points out that laymen and dilettantes can and often do discover mistakes in the most cherished views of the experts, and that moreover, expert opinion is often prejudiced, untrustworthy, and in need of outside control. (Beyond Reason: Essays on the Philosophy of Paul Feyerabend, edited by Gonzalo Muneyar, page 189)

Feyerabend's plea for democratic participation in scientific matters was directed against the dangers for a free society that came with the unregulated dominance, ignorance, and one-sidedness of the scientists in modern societies. Experts should be heard and listened to but they should not have the last word. (Nico Stehr, Knowledge Politics: Governing the Consequences of Science and Technology, page 128)

It is likely that the suppression of Dr. Rife's "Resonant Frequency" therapy for curing cancer will be recognized someday as one of the worst tragedies ever caused by a combination of self-interested, conventional scientists and government upper-management who got caught up in personal career ambitions while essentially forgetting the primacy of the public interest. Resulting in the unnecssary suffering and death of many millions of innocent people.

Rife therapy should be revived, thoroughly studied, honestly evaluated, clinically tested, and made available to any cancer patient who wants it.

It is a fair statement that Rife practically developed bioelectric medicine himself. There is a wide variation in the cost, design, and quality of the modern Rife frequency research instruments available ... One day the name of Royal Raymond Rife may ascend to its rightful place as the giant of modern medical science. Until that time, his fabulous technology remains available only to the people who have the interest to seek it out.

"Royal Raymond Rife: His Incredible Cancer Cure and the Successful Campaign to Suppress His Work" healthresearchbooks.com/articles/rife.htm

Appendix A

"Science cannot develop unless old certainties are queried. Taboos are the enemy of understanding."

The Economist **magazine, June 4, 2016, p. 10**

The nation's cancer program is fixed. It is a rigged system that promotes overpriced orthodox treatments that have failed for many, many decades. Alternative therapies are suppressed.

The cancer experts and the academic researchers take orders from a cabal of big money interests.

The authorities who run the cancer industry have never allowed "Resonant Frequency" therapy to be openly tested. They threatened its supporters. They attacked its supporters. They bribed its supporters to do something else. They used political muscle to protect the standard orthodoxies of cancer treatment -- surgery, radiation and chemotherapy.

Did the play-it-safe "scientific community" sell out the people of America to avoid finding the truth in order to keep favor with the special interest donors who paid for rigged results? They sure did. The money and privileges were too good to resist. To their everlasting shame because of the suffering that ensued. They will claim, "I didn't know." That's a feeble excuse.

Only a few successful tests of "Resonant Frequency" therapy could have devastated the monopolies kept in place by the "cancer industrial complex." Thus, the academic scientists stayed far, far away from doing honest research of this phenomenon of Nature -- destroying the microbe associated with cancer through a feedback method that was safe and non-invasive.

Instead, expensive orthodox treatments were kept in place. Few real medical alternatives were allowed for cancer patients. The system was controlled by big corporate profiteers, countless lobbyists

and government careerists who were part of the "professional class." They knew the rules and participated in the conferences and peer-reviewed journals' insider's club that kept true innovation out. Always refusing to examine a therapy that had actually cured cancer, with lots of documented evidence.

Someday it will all be exposed and its horrible cause -- big money control -- will be widely recognized for an evil that could have been prevented. The political class in Congress and in state governments dared not challenge the bosses of big medicine. They took the money and kept their heads down. Not a single state made itself into an "experimental" laboratory for an alternative treatment that had been amazingly successful with cancer in both doctors' offices and in a university-sponsored clinical trial. Yet "Resonant Frequency" therapy remained a taboo topic for the medical elite and the so-called media "watchdogs" supposedly serving the public. Such an all-around scam with a disease that causes so much suffering and death.

An entire new field of science is censored. Deliberately by powers who benefit from the status quo and also by a "science community" that fails to honor the principles of its discipline -- scientific integrity in the pursuit of truth.

The cancer "experts" never made any attempt to disprove "Resonant Frequency" therapy by simply doing honest testing. They just concealed its potential. No discussion, no independent study, no grants for even the most preliminary research, and absolutely no clinial trials because the method could not be patented! Sad for such exalted professionals holding all of those billions of dollars to

find the cause of and the cure for cancer.

Fiscal budget 2016 for the National Cancer Institute: 5+ billion dollars.

As for the "political class," they were clueless. Didn't hold any hearings, didn't have any interest in science breakthroughs linked to those very controversial "alternative" cures for cancer. So they supported the status quo and "conventional" treatments. After all, a lot of money came to them from big pharma for conducting their election campaigns. But the elected representatives are supposed to be "serving" the people's interest also, not just getting themselves elected. What could be more beneficial for the public good than finally allowing a safe, non-toxic therapy for cancer to be "allowed" for those who want it?

Someone should remind Congress that its members are hired to scrutinize what the cancer officials are up to and also what is on the forbidden list for this very "professional" class of public servants and managers who supposedly know "everything" about cancer.

Maybe the watchdogs from the press should be nosy "Focusing" on what the cancer elite avoid.

Any competent investigative reporter could confirm the fact that this method of "Resonant Frequency" therapy did cure cancer because the historical evidence is now very comprehensive. Any first-rate congressional investigator could easily look at the cold, hard truth. But apparently there was nobody in the government's cancer institutions (HHS, NCI) who cared to look. So it got "lost." Maybe they didn't want to know. Sure looks like medical politics prevented

any interest in this <u>demonstrated</u> cure.

Maybe a crime writer should check the evidence. Because the cancer establishment's refusal to investigate will be a monstrous crime if the "Resonant Frequency" therapy can cure many people of cancer. And it was "lost." Slipped through the cracks? The government's cracks. The academic scientists' cracks. The cancer centers' cracks. The investment cracks. Even the philanthropists' cracks. Never allowed to be openly tested. Strange.

"The conventional cancer treatment system and the pharmaceutical companies that control it are dedicated to limiting the development of all other forms of cancer treatment. They have a stranglehold on the development of alternative treatments, and they ruthlessly work together with the US FDA and various US government cancer research funding agencies to prevent new treatments from being approved for use by physicians ... The great fear of the pharmaceutical industry and the vast cancer treatment system that it controls, is that a non-patentable and inexpensive cure for cancer might put them out of business ..."

("A Review of Alternative Cancer Therapies" by John P. Thomas, healthimpactnews.com)

How Simple The Science If The Experts Dared To Look

"There appear granulations, called 'dwarf forms', of very small dimensions, measuring in fact a millionth of a millimeter ... They seem to be rather fragile and possess a very special property, due to their smallness, of being able to go through the walls of filters which retain normal bacteria." (Alan Deanay, *The World of Microbes*, 1965, page 43.)

"... owing to the minuteness of these particles, it is impossible to stain them with any known method or technique using acid or aniline stains; hence a substitute stain was found ... a frequency of light that coordinates with the chemical constituents of the particle or micro-organism under observation." (Royal Rife, *History of the Development of a Successful Treatment for Cancer*, 1953.)

The science is breathtakingly simple. Disease conditions can be identified by unique wavelengths that define colors. Scientists estimate that humans can recognize "10 million shades of color". (*National Geographic*, Oct 2001, page 17.)

"We can make a positive diagnosis of any disease from which the filtered forms can be observed ... checked 181 times against a color dictionary to see if the color of the various forms would change a shade or two but they have been found to be very constant." (Royal Rife, paper titled "Cultivation", 1954.)

"... this special illumination reveals the filter passing organism in characteristic individual colors ... no two kinds or forms of organisms have been found to have the same colors." (*San Diego Evening Tribune* newspaper, May 11, 1938.)

APPENDIX B

"The true and legitimate goal of the Sciences is to endow human life with new discoveries and resources."

Francis Bacon (1561-1626)

From *NEW ORGANUM* (from Greek "instrument" or "tool") artsofliberty.org

Royal Rife's Universal Microscope and his Frequency Instrument therapy would have delighted Francis Bacon.

"Bacon has been called ... the father of scientific method. This marked a new turn in the rhetorical and theoretical framework for science." Wikipedia

Looking Back ...

And Forward?

"The future of medicine is in light and electromagnetic fields. Once we find a way of manipulating and controlling electromagnetic fields, we will be able to cure just about any disease. Probably the guy who knew the most was Royal Raymond Rife." (Donald J. Hess, *Evaluating Alternative Cancer Therapies*, Rutgers University Press.)

****

"If you have a biological treatment that really creates a good response in human cancer patients, you know this without a randomized control trial. You don't need it for a breakthrough." (Patrick McGrady, Jr., *Cancer Scandal*, one hour videotape.)

****

"The key to fighting cancer and other diseases successfully lies in the potential of destroying the pathogenic microorganisms and getting the body to excrete them. The microbial activity is the basis for the growth process of the tumor.

"The remedies can heal the individual at any stage in the growth process if the microbial progression is reversed." (Michael Coyle, *Advanced Microscopy for Nutritional Evaluation and Correction*.)

****

"The virus form ... is one phase in the life history of many, if not all, bacteria. The bacterial forms do not produce cancer, but the virus form does." The renowned Canadian cancer expert O. C. Gruner, who worked and corresponded with Royal Rife for many years. From his book *Study of Blood in Cancer*.)

"Royal Raymond Rife studied medicine at the prestigious Johns Hopkins University and began his career as a research pathologist and medical researcher ... Rife became probably the first person ever to fulfill Koch's postulates for cancer causing microbes. Koch's postulates are a set of rules to prove the causation of disease by microorganisms ...

"The cancer virus which Rife named ... the BX virus was a minute 1/5 micron in length and 1/20 micron in width ... While the discovery of a cancer virus was in itself an incredible feat of scientific endeavor, Rife was to make yet more discoveries destined to rock the scientific status quo."

(alternative-cancer-cure.com)

****

"The result of using a resonant wavelength is that micro-organisms which are invisible in white light suddenly become visible in a brilliant flash of light when they are exposed to the color frequency that resonates with their own spectroscopic signature. Dr. Royal Rife was thus able to see these otherwise invisible organisms ... Dr. Royal Rife's discovery enabled him to view organisms that no one else could see with ordinary microscopes.

"Royal Rife ... was a well known scientist because of his breakthrough invention of an extremely powerful microscope and he was very successful in curing certain diseases. He was highly regarded within the scientific community until the medical establishment came down on him and erased him from history ... the threat to orthodox medicine was too great. Medical officials and societies mounted a furious counterattack against Rife's monumental discovery before the American public could be informed of it. One of the greatest scientific and medical discoveries of the 20th century was ruthlessly shoved into a dungeon of history."

(Soul-guidance.com/health/rife/htm.

"Rife's system allowed adjusting the frequency of light inpinging on the specimen. By some insight he learned that the light frequency could be 'tuned' into the natural frequency of the microorganism being examined to cause a resonance or feed-back loop. In effect, under this condition, it can be said the microorganism illuminated itself."

John W. Mattingly, professor, inventor, and microbiology investigator who wrote the foreword to *The Cancer Cure That Worked: The Rife Report*

An honest cancer establishment and particularly the U. S. government agencies and organizations responsible for the nation's cancer policies and programs -- NCI, FDA, HHS -- would have conducted fair, objective studies and tests of Rife's unique discoveries out of curiousity and dedication to preserving the scientific standards that support truth seeking principles and basic citizen rights or the public interest.

But the government's cancer establishment and the private cancer centers did the opposite. It attacked all natural and alternative therapies because the moneyed interests had a stranglehold on what cancer treatments could be used and what professional specialists and cancer products were "approved".

The cancer industry was corrupt and rigged to serve monopoly interests. It needs deep transformation. "Resonance Frequency" therapy has been kept off-limits for many decades. It could destroy the existing cancer racket and cure millions of cancer patients.

Any competent investigator could have checked the historical record and documented results and quickly realized that cancer had been cured in a significant number of cases by doctors using Rife's new science and revolutionary therapy. But the "professional classes" operating in the corridors of the cancer institutions and laboratories were too busy, too comfortable, and too political to risk challenging the group think. Tragic when the countless lives lost are considered in analyzing the deliberate non-actions of the management class.

In November 2016, CBS's Charlie Rose, while receiving a journalism award from his peers, declared for his profession that "truth shall prevail" if journalists do their job. One wonders if his profession will dare to investigate the suppression of the science and cancer therapy known as "Resonance Frequency" destruction of cancer-causing micro-organisms of virus size. As Dr. Rife demonstrated so long ago!

"Rife Therapy and Treatment Explained

Rife Healing Medicine: Suppressed and Misunderstood"

Alternativemedicinetruth.blogspot.ca March 17, 2007 casperdude

"Rife frequency therapy, put simply, is a term for the use of ultrasound to kill germs ... Most every germ or pathogen has its own resonant frequency at which it will vibrate and shake until its structure is disrupted ... Once the basic principles of this science are grasped, it is quite easy to see how this really works and how it can be applied to all manner of pathogen-based diseases.

"The applications of this are so wide and so effective that even in Rife's day, the orthodox authorities such as the FDA and the AMA fought hard and long to keep this science away from the public's awareness.

"Rife is currently being used by doctors in Germany and all over the world in conjunction with other effective therapies that have been declared illegal in the USA."

Roy Rife Reflects

From *The Cancer Cure That Worked: The Rife Report*

Quoted on Whale.com run by Jon Whale

Rife said:

"In reality, it is not the bacteria themselves that produce the disease, but the chemical constituents of those micro-organisms enacting upon the unbalanced cell metabolism of the human body that in actuality produce the disease. We also believe if the metabolism of the human body is perfectly balanced or poised, it is susceptible to no disease."

After isolating the cancer virus, his next step was to destroy it. He did this with his frequency instruments -- over and over again. And then he did it with experimental animals, inoculating them, watching the tumors grow, and then killing the virus in their bodies with the same frequency instruments tuned to the same "BX" frequency.

XXX

Physicist Gary Wade Explains the Unique Qualities of Rife's Universal Microscope

In 1931, after seven years of attempting to isolate a microbe cause of cancer from over 20,000 cancer tissue samples, Dr. Royal Rife did just that. Rife's 1931 discovery of a cancer microbe finally reached general public notice in 1944. That year an article titled "The New Microscopes" was published in the February issue of *The Journal of the Franklin Institute* and the *1944 Annual Report* of the Board of Directors of the Smithsonian Institute.

Rife's work was not then and has not yet been appreciated by microbiology because microbiology has a large blind spot, both in its physical visual view of the living microworld and in its conceptual view of the structure and life cycles of the living microworld. If you wish to look at living cells, the best research optical microscopes generally available throughout the world only reach about three thousand power. These microscopes in general cannot detect viruses, unless a fluorescence technique like Rife's fluorescence technique is used. These microscopes give very limited structural detail about living cell organisms.

If the biologist wants detailed structural information about some cell structure, they use an electron microscope. However, the electron microscope picture is the picture of a dead, often highly degraded and distorted structure. This is because the sample preparation process, which produces a sample that can withstand the conditions of high vacuum and bombardment by a high energy electron beam has degraded and distorted the original living structure. So at best you end up with a distorted snap shot of a non-living structure.

... Rife had discovered an optical assembly configuration that effectively

suppressed all Fraunhofer diffraction phenomenon while at the same time he made the organism light itself by a natural fluorescence phenomenon. The fluorescence phenomenon was achieved by illuminating the specimen with an intense narrow wavelength band of light. The particular band of light was unique to each microbe.

If you are familiar with current microbiology, you know that little if any time is spent by the great majority of researchers watching and studying live microbes ... In short, actually very little live observation on microbe life cycles are carried out by researchers anywhere in the world.

... no currently trained microbiologist owns or uses a Rife type optical microscope which could easily view ... BX cancer virus.

"Great Revolutionary Leaders of Alternative Medicine: A Fascinating Journey Back in Time"

By Richard C. Memtzow, M.D., Ph.D., M.P.H.

"John Hubbard, M.D., a pathologist and an associate professor of pathology at the State University of New York, Buffalo, provides the answer concerning the validity of this controversial (Rife) microscope.

"Hubbard: (The photographs that were published in the 1944 Smithsonian Report) 'are indisputably beyond the capability of any resolution that was available at the time, and they have been confirmed by electron microscope since then ... you see the spacing between these lines have ... the distances ... the instrument that produced this was able to produce a resolution which we were not able to obtain except with the electron microscope many years later.'

" 'This has resolution down in the neighborhood of about 20 angstroms , at least, and nobody had ever been able to do that ... All you have to do is the arithmetic, the object size, the size of the specimen times the magnification, is equal to the image size. So if we have the image size we can do the arithmetic and we can go back and figure out what the object size was ... We know what the diameter of tetanos spores are, from both light microscopes (the conventional light microscope) and from the electron microscope. By going back and checking the arithmetic from that ... source, we can confirm that this is the correct dimension. We can compare the distance and we get a ratio, which is exactly comparable to what we know from modern electron microscopy.'"

(The article appeared originally in *The Journal of Alternative and Complementary Medicine*, August 2002.)

Requiem for Royal Rife by Shawn Montgomery

lifetechnologynewsblogspot.com **August 12, 2006**

Excerpt:

It was in the mid 1940[s that a young student of pathology first became obsessed with the Rife Universal Microscope. John Hubbard, keeping up with current advancements in the tools of his chosen trade, was thumbing through the ... Journal of the Smithsonian Institute when he came upon the artitle titled "The New Microscopes." In astonishment, he read of Rife's instrument -- a microscope that appeared to defy the accepted limits of optics. At face value the text of the article seemed somewhat incredible. However, three photomicrographs included therein, taken through the Universal Microscope, tempered Hubbard's incredulity.

The published photos were all labeled with magnification values: Chlorophyll (Cell) 17,000 X, Tetanus (Spore) 25,000 X, Typhoid Bacillus (B. Typhosus) 23,000 X. Hubbard recognized the extraordinary feature of the pictures, the uncanny resolution of detail, the fantastic magnification values (one order higher than standard optical scopes), the clear imaging of certain structural features within the specimens (the existence of which had previously only been suspected by microbiologists -- never seen and confirmed).

Here it was, the ultimate microscope. A tool that could crack open the still-murky world of germs and spill all of the remaining secrets out onto the table. A tool that could help answer just about any question a microbiologist could ask ...

From *The Guardian* newspaper of London, England -- April 2, 2003.

"Dr. Rife's Oscillating Beam Ray" by Mark Pilkington:

"In the early 1930s, Dr. Royal Rife, an American optics engineer, claimed to be achieving theoretically impossible optical magnifications of over 30,000 times -- 10 times more powerful than today's best microscopes.

"Rife announced that he could destroy bacteria by blasting them with electromagnetic waves oscillating at frequencies specific to each target organism ... his most controversial claim was that his device would kill the virus-like organisms ... responsible for cancer.

"Rife's ray tube system was installed in several clinics and his results were corroborated by numerous scientists and doctors. In 1939 he was invited to address the Royal Society of Medicine, which had also approved his findings, and he subsequently formed the Rife Ray Beam Tube Corporation, to build models for hospitals and clinics ... Rife found himself under sudden and prolonged assault from the American Medical Society ...

"... an English group claimed to have found a 1939 beam ray walled up in a doctor's surgery ... If the UK team can get the Rife device operational we may yet see a beam ray in every home and Royal Rife will get the place in history ... he deserved."

(NOTE: Rife's Universal Microscope did achieve the magnification that he claimed. As shown by micro-photos published in the *Smithsonian Institute Annual Report*. 30 YEARS before the electron microscope was able to verify Rife's accomplishment. The "theoretically impossible" magnification was reached and the evidence can be studied on the internet by anyone who wants to see for themselves the first ever photos of those tiny living microbes.)

From *The Medical Racket* by Wade Frazier, June 2014

One problem with microscope investigation into biology is the microscope itself. The wave length of visible light is the theoretical limiting factor in optical microscopes. The smaller the wavelength of light shined upon something, the finer the image resolution. Resolution of optical microscopes is traditionally described in terms of diameters. The limit of optical microscopes has been around 2,000 - 2,500 diameters for many years. It does not matter how fine your lenses are, and it does not matter how hard you look, 2,000 - 2,500 is the limit of optical microscopes, because of the wavelength of visible light, which is about 4,000 angstroms.

... a San Diego biologist was developing a microscope that today stands as one of biology's greatest breakthroughs. Royal Rife ... stands among science's giants.

Modern optical theory cannot explain how Rife's microscope worked ... His 1933 Universal Microscope attained a resolution of 31,000 diameters. Although anti-Rife propaganda has circulated since the 1930s, and his microscope is dismissed by orthodoxy today, images taken with his microscope survive, which proves the "impossible" results that Rife's microscope achieved.

Peering deeper into the microbiological milieu than anyone had ever done before, Rife clearly ... was able to see his specimens *in vivo*. In watching life processes under unprecedented magnification, Rife accomplished a feat that has still not been reproduced by orthodox science nearly a century later.

Besides isolating the cancer virus (something never before seen) Rife had also proven the pleomorphic theory of microbiology first elucidated by Bechamp. In 1932, Rife was using his frequency device to destroy the typhus bacteria, the poliovirus, the herpes virus, the cancer virus, and others using experimental animals. Human treatment was not far off.

The Extraordinary Story of Royal Rife

by Holly Cornish at cancerdefeated.com May 18, 2016

Cancer Defeated P.O. Box 1076, Lexington, VA 24450

Publisher of Information About Alternative Cancer Treatments

Excerpt:

Mr. Rife was an American self-educated inventor who became interested in the biological effects of electromagnetic fields and whether they had any therapeutic value.

The Universal Microscope he built in 1933 had a magnification of 60,000. This was over 20 times greater than existing microscopes of his day and went well beyond the known laws of physics ...

Such magnification allowed him to see pathogens in their live state, something never seen before ... he developed a way to view biological samples without staining them. Every pathogen has a different electro-magnetic frequency and each appears as a different shade of color.

To honor Dr. Rife and Kendall, a banquet was organized at Dr. Johnson's home and 30 of the most eminent medical figures in Southern California were invited to celebrate "The End to All Diseases." The *Los Angeles Times* reported:

Frankly dubious about the perfection of a microscope which appears to transcend the limits set by optical science, Dr. Johnson's guests expressed themselves as delighted with the demonstration and heartily accorded both Mr. Rife and Kendall a foremost place in the world's rank of scientists.

The Rife Microscope, or "Facts and Their Fate"

A Summary of articles by Dr. Royal Lee and by R. E. Seidel, MD, and M. Elizabeth Winter which appeared in journals in 1944 and 1955. From Selene River Press at website seleneriverpress.com.

Excerpt:

The Rife Microscope is one of the most fascinating and tragic stories in the history of science. Royal Rife was a genius of optics who in the 1930s invented a revolutionary microscope that identified micro-organisms based on a characteristic wavelength of light emitted by each. (Rife discovered these "signature emissions" through use of his scope.)

... Rife not only collaborated with noted bacteriologist Dr. Arthur Kendall of Northwestern University Medical School to demonstrate such transformations, but the two investigators showed they were able to destroy pathogen forms by radiating them with wavelengths of light in resonance with their signature emission.

When Rife began to publish his findings, he was predictably branded a quack by the medical establishment which brought its full efforts to discredit and destroy his work. All references and studies involving his microscope were actively barred from medical journals.

... the potential applications of Rife's long lost microscope are beyond profound.

From Video: *The Rise and Fall of a Scientific Genius*

by Rife Research Group of Canada

"Rife was a master tool maker ... He was also a visionary ... The Universal Microscope is a revolutionary breakthrough in optics."

Michael Coyle, microscopist

"It's an amazing, wondrous feat." James Bare, DC

"Here was something with enormous potential for humanity's sake." Bert Comparet, Rife's attorney

"What little we have done will be a stepping stone for science workers in the future." Royal Rife

"The Wonderwork of 1931" by Ransom Sutton

From *Los Angeles Times Magazine*, December 27, 1931

Excerpt:

If the experimental results obtained at the Pasadena Hospital by Dr. Arthur I. Kendall, bacteriologist of Northweatern University, and Dr. Royal R. Rife of San Diego test true, man now has the knowledge and the weapon which will enable him to win the war against disease breeding germs ... The story is almost unbelievable.

Having heard about a "wonder microscope," said to have been invented by a young San Diegan, Dr. Kendall asked his friend Dr. Milbank Johnson of Los Angeles, if such a microscope existed ... Dr. Johnson ... drove to San Diego and found Dr. Rife and a new kind of microscope ... Designed on a new plan entirely, this microscope has six quartz lenses, giving it a magnifying power eight times greater than the high powered-microscopes used by physicists.

Dr. Milbank Johnson arrnaged for Dr. Kendall and Dr. Rife to get together at the Pasadena Hospital where, we were told by both Dr. Kendall and Dr. Rife, the super microscope brought Kendall's "seeds of life," distinctly within range of human vision. A bacillus or bacterium -- a single cell organism -- was seen to be made up of "granules," like the separate grains in a head of wheat, each granule being a free, motile, living thing.

... each kind of granule ... has -- under polarized light -- a distinctive color of its own, thereby enabling bacteriologist to diagnose germ-diseases by the color of the germs. Bacilli may thus be studied by their light, exactly as astronomers study moons, suns and other stars by the light which comes from them through telescopes. The bacilli studied are living ones, not corpses killed by stains.

So extraordinary are these statements that scientists generally would regard them as visionary, or scientifically impossible, if they were not vouched for by such distinguished authorities ... The physicists and astronomers with whom I have discussed the matter are not yet convinced ... The absolute limit beyond which microscopes cannot go has been defined in these words, "any object smaller than half of the wavelength of the light by which it is illuminated cannot be seen in its true form and size owing to diffraction."

On the other hand, this is a new kind of magnifier, and the laws governing microscopes may not apply to it ... 250 scientists present ... the impression prevailed that Dr. Rife, a 44 year "wizard" ... has developed an instrument that may revolutionize laboratory methods and enable bacteriologists, like Dr. Kendall, to identify the germs that produce 50 diseases whose cause are unknown ... then to find ways and means to immunize mankind against them.

"Doctors Wait For Test Of Rife Ray" by Newall Jones

From *San Diego Evening Tribune* newspaper, May 7, 1938

Excerpt:

Royal Raymond Rife, San Diego scientist .. told of the latest developments made in his Pt. Loma laboratory on his microscope, the first of which was announced seven years ago, and of unreported discoveries which these have made possible. Outstanding among these discoveries were the revelations of previously unseen, filter-passing, pathogenic viruses for bombardment with the Rife Ray.

"Physicists always have clung to the rule," said the San Diegan, "that any object which is smaller than one-half the wavelength of the light by which it is illuminated under the microscope cannot be seen in its true form or detail." This is true with the conventional method of optics. But these instruments introduce other methods."

The scientist explained the new methods and what they accomplish.

In the standard microscope, the image of the subject being studied is projected 180 millimeters from the master lens of the objective to the eye point. By this great distance of projection, the magnification is limited.

However, in the optical principles involved in the Rife instruments, there is virtually a tube length of 200 to 449 millimeters, but the greatest distance of projection of the image through any one media, either quartz or air, is less than 30 millimeters.

This shortening of the distance through any one media, it was explained, allows greater magnification and eliminates chromatical, and most of the spherical aberration ... This shortening is made possible by use of quartz blocks and prisms in the body tube of the microscope to carry the vision of the image through the optical path. In the conventional microscope, the vision of the image passes through the air in the hollow tube of the instrument.

The new instruments obtain in this manner a peak magnification of 31,000. Maximum for standard laboratory instruments is only slightly more than 1600.

Then, in making visible the filter-passing forms of bacteria, or virus, the paramount factor of the Rife instrument is a different illuminating system, the major part of which is composed of a series of rotating, circular wedged quartz prisms. As these prisms are rotated, they increase or decrease the angle of incidence or the illuminating beam, changing the light beam frequency, or wavelength, to coordinate with the particular organism under observation.

"Presenting A Brief History of the Evolution of the Microscope"

By Royal Rife

From *The Aerohcrafter* (a corporate newsletter/journal) Jan 1954

Excerpt:

"Anthony Von Leeuwenhoek, justly called the father of microscopy, was born in Delft, Holland in 1632. Von Leeuwenhoek built all his own microscopes, preferring the single lens to the compound type ... He described many small living particles in such minute detail that we know them today as bacteria ... his findings ... were presented to the Royal Society of London in 1683 ... there remains little doubt that Von Leeuwenhoek with his primitive lens had observed the bodies now recognized as the cause of disease ...

"In 1870, (Ernst) Abbe, the immortal optical wizard of the Carl Zeiss works in Jena (Germany), developed and brought out the sub-stage condenser, which still bears his name, and was one of the outstanding contributions to the microscope of all time. From 1880 to 1885, Carl Zeiss introduced many improvements in the microscope. Among them the appocromat objective lens, which was an outstanding optical achievement at that time.

"Thus the microscope has steadily risen out of the dim mist of antiquity to the modern instruments of the present day. The writer, over a period of thirty years, has designed and built in his own laboratory 5 microscopes of power and resolution far beyond the so-called law of optical physics. These instruments vary in their power from 17 to 50,000 times above and beyond the limits of the standard research instrument. The commerical microscope being manufactured is inadequate for the observation of filterable viruses of disease (as these minute, live, living entities are less than 1/20 of one micron in dimension). Thus the need for a device which would carry us farther into this important field of endeavor. We will describe in some detail the most important of these microscopes, known as the universal microscope ...

Rife's History of Microscopes (continued)

"When the quartz prisms on the universal microscope ... are rotated in opposite directions, they serve to bend the transmitted beams of light at variable angles of incidence while, at the same time, a spectrum is projected up into the axis of the microscope ... Now, when a portion of the spectrum is reached in which both the organism and the color band vibrate in exact accord, one with the other, a definite characteristic spectrum is emitted by the organism ... thus enabling the observer to view the organism stained in its true chemical color and revealing its own individual structure in a field which is brilliant with light.

"... The fine adjustment being 700 times more sensitive than the ordinary microscope, the length of time required to focus the universal microscope ... may seem a disadvantage ... but a slight inconvenience when compared with the many years of research ... spent in an effort to isolate and to look upon disease-causing organisms in their true form.

"We sincerely hope that our efforts in the field of optics, and its allied branches, will stimulate and create a desire in the minds of other workers to carry on the broad and inviting field before us, one which presents a work so vital and essential for the benefit of all mankind."

****

This entire article from *The Aerohcrafter* of January 1954, providing Rife's own technical description of the Universal Microscope, is available at RifeVideos.com.   Designing and building the Universal Microscope was an awesome accomplishment.

A Top Scientist at the Mayo Clinic Publishes the Fact that He Has Witnessed a Rife Microscope Achieve Record-Breaking Levels of Magnification and Resolution

In the August 26, 1932 issue of *Science*, the most prestigious journal of science in America, Edward C. Rosenow announced that during a 3-day use of a Rife microscope on July 5 - 7, 1932, he and Arthur Kendall of Northwestern University Medical School in Chicago saw the Rife Microscope achieve a magnification of 8,000 diameters.

"Dr. Rosenow was generally regarded in prominent medical circles as among the most brilliant of modern scientists." He served "as head of experimental bacteriology for the Mayo Foundation for nearly three decades from 1915 to 1944" according to a tribute to Rosenow by S. H. Shakman in a publication for the Institute of Science in the late 1990s.

Rosenow declared for the historical record in his *Science* journal report that he could clearly observe micro-organisms at nine times what a standard microscope could show:

"Their visualization under the Rife microscope is due to the ingenius methods employed ... Examination under the Rife microscope of specimens, containing objects visible with the ordinary microscope, leaves no doubt of the accurate visualization of objects or particulate matter by high magnification (calculated to be 8,000 diameters) obtained with this instrument."

Yet today, in the 2nd decade of the 21st century, numerous internet skeptics declare that Rife's microscope was a fake because of the wavelength of light's limitations, blah, blah, blah. These smug naysayers -- of course! -- never bother to check the scientific literature. They defend the orthodox dogma and any statements to the contrary -- even by highly qualified masters in the field! -- will be disregarded, denounced, and loudly defined as "impossible". But Rife lived in an "impossible" world. And left micro-photos for future explorers who will follow him into the micro world and confirm what Rife discovered.

From Bruce Forrester at website zephyrtechnology.com:

"As with many great inventors, Rife found himself persecuted and he died a broken man, leaving behind the legacy of his great accomplishments for future generations to rediscover.

"Rife began his research looking for an unknown cause for cancer ...

"The first step was to image the living virus in some way that allowed a magnification great enough and resolution clear enough that a human eye could perceive the very mechanisms that were the wheelworks of the cancer process ... the problem with a normal light optics in magnifying microscopes is that the wavelength of the source light prohibits the imaging of items that have a diameter that is smaller. You simply cannot image an object that is smaller than the source light wavelength!

"But by resonating cells to the point that they become the light source, Rife was able to construct one of his greatest inventions ... the *Rife Universal Microscope* ... a microscope that allowed optical imaging of living things as small as a virus while they were active and 'alive.' He discovered things never before seen by a human being."

Appendix C

The Crazy, Ascending, Accelerating World of Rife. Chasing That Starship.

Rife Lives On

Ken Welch, August 31, 1999, abchomeopathy.com

"On August 19th (1999) ... the first American patient began treatment at an experimental clinic in Georgia (Europe) where a multidisciplinary team is attempting to reproduce ... a Russian trial program ... from beyond the medical mainstream ... These results are in the published proceedings of the 1999 Scientific and Technological Conferences, an annual event in Moscow, sponsored by the Russian Ministry of Foreign Affairs.

"The word from Georgia insiders is that lab results on the first batch of patients is pretty exciting, although astounding might be a better word, given the mode of treatment. Patients received only an IV drip of -- believe it or not -- the same standard saline solution used in hospitals around the world. The difference is that the IV solution carries a special charge or resonance. In a surprise blending of Homeopathy and the pioneering research of Royal Rife. Rife demonstrated the destruction of disease organisms by broadcast energy at specific frequencies. Today, a new twist takes his work another step forward.

"... Rife used a form of broadcast energy, created in a neon-like florescent tube, to apply frequencies to person's whole body. His premise was that the right frequency could cause the death of a specific target organism, and thus eliminate a specific disease. He arrived at this by actually observing the destruction of viruses in a unique microscope he invented using the same broadcast concepts.

"With his microscope, Rife had the advantage of being able to tune his device and confirm the correct frequency simply by observing the result.

"... the Russian team apparently combined technologies to create a scientific breakthrough. While the devices and technology are protected by patent and the subject of considerable secrecy, it is apparent that several problems have been solved. These involve the selection of what specific

frequency or resonance will be effective and the method of "charging" water molecules with that energy to create a viable delivery system.

"The second breakthrough is in the delivery system, both in theory and in practice. The Russians see their frequency selection as an opposite or "canceling" frequency, rather than the more direct, "destructive" frequency which Rife observed when microorganisms glowed and shattered in the field of his microscope...

"The Russian theory is that an invading virus ... has a certain frequency, and that by bathing this pathogen in something carrying an "opposite" frequency the result is a zero sum: the organism's energy is neutralized and the virus dies."

Star Trek Medicine -- Bioresonance

Dr. Mark Sircus, December 4, 2013. DrSircus.com

"Thought doctor McCoy had it good with his equipment on the Starship Enterprise? Wait until you get a load of what is coming to revolutionize the world of medicine ... The future has arrived and just as three-dimensional printing will revolutionize manufacturing, this technology will revolutionize the practice of medicine.

"This groundbreaking technology ... destroying the pharmaceutcal paradigm and the doctors that practice it, using electromedicine vibration to ... cure without side effects.

"President Putin of Russia uses it and the Department of Health in Russia has approved it for wide use across their nation, which amounts to three hundred million.

"This phenomenon where we can kill microbes with frequencies is called BIORESONANCE.

"Can you see the power of this? Once diagnosed with a particular parasite or virus it can be targeted with a particular frequency that will no harm to anything else but the kill the parasite / virus.

"There have been many researchers that have worked on energy medicine and Bioresonance this past century such as Dr. Rife ... and others."

Extraordinary Biology by Tom Beardon at website <u>cheniere.org</u>

<u>Royal Raymond Rife</u>

In the 1930's and 1940's, Royal Raymond Rife revolutionized everything that has been done before or since in high resolution optical microscopy.

He also revolutionized everything before or since in cellular biology. He carried cellular structure far beyond anything ever dreamed of in his time or presently. He revealed the direct connection between organized living energy forms and organized biological systems. He revealed that life itself is organized and dynamic, to a far finder level than anything in the textbooks today. <u>He revealed that our present theory of disease is fundamentally very, very wrong</u>.

He produced direct, economical, electromagnetic cures of cancer, leukemia and other such debilitating diseases. His work presages a future mankind could have had, where most debilitating diseases were quickly and economically corrected, and where no poisonous drugs, violent nuclear irradiation, and harsh chemotherapeutic "burning" of the patient would be necessary.

For such epochal work, he was ostracized, essentially imprisoned in a medical treatment facility, broken, condemned, and rejected by his peers. His findings, though printed in reputable publications and journals, was discredited and ridiculed.

He literally was reduced to a non-person by the power of the medical cartel.

With his Universal Microscope, Rife ... could examine living viruses, living bacteria, and other as-yet-undiscovered living organisms and living energy forms that no other microscope before or since could see ...

Rife had advanced biology and biophysics a century in one jump ...

He died without ever being vindicated for his marvelous, world-shaking discoveries.

Unariunwisdom.com by Gerry Vassilatos

Exerpt:

The Rife ultra-microscope was about to trigger a war on viruses. Because of the self-fluorescent "staining" method, Dr. Rife observed live specimens exclusively; a distinguishing feature of his technology. The fluorescent coloration of each pathogen was catalogued, an historic endeavor. Tuberculosis bacilli appeared emerald green, leprosy was ruby red, E. Coli were mahogany colored ... each wickedly deceptive in their pretty colors. The degree of precision demonstrated in Dr. Rife's catalogues bears the unmistakable mark of genius. We can view him at work in the archival movies.

The prismatic microscope was piercing into new shadows. Dr. Rife recognized virus species everywhere. And then he turned his vision into the deepest shadow. He looked at the dreaded disease. To this very day the very utterance of the disease is foul. It carries the nimbus of finality. Cancer ... All who speak its name whisper in fear, afraid that it will hear and come for them ... "the evil sickness."

Dr. Rife began obtaining a wide variety of malignant tissue in 1931. The full power of the first Prismatic Microscope was turned on those tissue samples with a vengeance. Dr. Rife was a master pathologist ... what were those motile forms, glowing with a beautiful violet-red coloration? ...

Examination of each separate sample under the Prismatic Microscope revealed a consistent truth. There they were again! Always the same violet-red presence. He called it the BX virus, finding it present in every case of cancer in humans ... There could be no mistake. Independent acquisition of tissue samples were obtained by others who then verified those findings in distant laboratories.

He succeeded in isolating the BX virus in 1931, filming the process so that posterity would hopefully learn of its enemy ... Soon, the ray had done its work on the once-terminal victims. Constant blood and tissue samples revealed no BX viral presence in those now fortunate individuals. In sixty days treatment time, and after examining by several physicians, each was released as cured.

Cancer Blow Seen After 18-year Toil by Rife

by Newall Jones

San Diego Evening Tribune, May 6, 1938

Full article available at Rifevideos.com

Excerpt:

Discovery that disease organisms, including one occurring in dread cancer, can be killed by bombarding them with radio waves tuned to a particular length for each kind of organism was claimed today by a San Diego scientist Royal Raymond Rife.

... Rife built better, better and better machines for generating the frequencies and directing them upon the tiny enemies of the human race. Now, he reported, the mortal oscillatory rates for many, many organisms has been found and recorded and the ray can be tuned to a germ's recorded frequency and turned upon that organism with assurance that the organism will be killed.

Inseparably linked with the ray development, Rife added, were two others almost equal in importance to the other discovery. These were a search for filter passing viruses, those minute disease causing substances which sneak through the finest filters which scientists can make and so are extremely difficult to capture and study, and the designing and building of a microscope which would reveal to his eye viruses never seen before. Both undertakings were successful, Rife commented. Eight years ago he began hunting the viruses with his microscope ... One of these previously undiscovered organisms, the scientist said, was that which is found in human carcinoma, or cancer.

... He saw on the slide a number of moving red-purple granules, the tiniest bits of microscopic life ever seen, only one-twentieth of a micron in length, so tiny that 500,000 of them placed end to end would span only the length of an inch on a ruler, he reported.

Healthoptimist.com

"My name is John Schleif, and I am a practitioner and researcher of frequency medicine ... Frequency therapy is based on the theory that all things are energy based and have a resonant frequency. You have probably heard of the example of an opera singer breaking a glass with the right pitch.

"Well, imagine if you have the right pitch or frequency of a bacteria or other microbe. A researcher in the 1930's studied this and found many micro-organisms could be destroyed with the right frequency; his name was Royal Rife.

"I'm also fortunate to have learned some effective techniques having studied with one of the leaders and pioneers in the field -- Dr. Jeff Sunterland."

****

Max Planck was the originator of quantum physics. He gave a lecture in December 1900 that changed physics forever. He was awarded a Nobel Prize for his discovery. Max Planck stated:

Everything is a vibration and its effect. In actuality, no physical matter can exist. All the physical matters are composed of vibrations.

Max Planck and Royal Rife saw a very similar reality. The world's medical schools, clinics and hospitals will be joining them in the 21st century.

Dr. Jeff Sunterland Responds to the Internet About Frequency Foundation

January 25, 2012 agilescout.com

"My stated goal for 20 years has been to change the world of medicine just as we have changed the world of software development ... My goal is to do the same thing with a device that costs about the same as a personal computer (and has no radiation exposure). We need a younger version of Bill Gates to lead the charge.

"I have a Ph.D. in this area, 11 years on the faculty of the University of Colorado Medical School funded by the National Cancer Institude, much published research, and am still, the last time I checked, one of only 300 scientists in the U. S. authorized to lead grants funded by NCI."

Dr. Jeff Sunterland Preface to The Rife Handbook Of Frequency Therapy by Nenah Sylver:

"Frequency therapy, properly applied, may well replace every other modality. Frequency devices can change the medical paradigm as we know it. But unfortunately, there is considerable resistance to electro-medicine.

"Healthcare is a government regulated monopoly that systematically suppresses new innovation ... powerful institutional forces fight simpler alternatives to expensive care because those alternatives threaten their livelihoods ... large amounts of money are involved."

Mercuryb ... March 13, 2012 healingwell.com

"rifing is based on the work of Dr. Rife who used frequencies to kill cancer. This does work as long as you find the right frequency for the right bug-viral ... There is a lot of medical research going on regarding these frequency machines now."

****

Incompetent, corrupt and criminal interests in the private sector and at state and federal government levels are keeping people from having access to the wonderful world of frequency therapy. The public needs to reclaim its basic healthcare rights.

****

"Monopoly Medicine is a Killer"

By Dr. Mark Sircus Drsircus.com September 22, 2014

"As free as many Americans might think they are, there are certain glaring aspects of American life for which individuals are not free to make their own choices, and cancer treatment is one of them. In the sobering documentary *Cut Poison Burn*, filmmaker Wayne Chesler brings to light the sinister nature of the multi-billion dollar cancer industry, its suppression of any real pursuit of a cure, and its stranglehold on medicine that restricts individuals from choosing their own personalized, alternative forms of treatment."

Medical Racketeering

It is appalling how crimes that maim and destroy so many cancer patients can remain politically "invisible" for so long. How they are not discussed in the mainstream media. It is an American tragedy and scandal, yet virtual censorship of the subject remains in place.

Lots of Americans are aware that the ruling elements of the "cancer industry" are involved in a criminal enterprise. But until the situation reaches a critical mass, it won't erupt into a crisis of public confidence that forces deep transformation of a system that emphasizes health instead of profit at the expense of health. The current structure of medicine has become a perversion of what medical science principles require.

The pharmaceutical cartel controls the medical schools. Why should this abomination be allowed to continue?

The pharmaceutical cartel controls the FDA, the NCI, the NIH and HHS (the Department of Health and Human Services). Drugs as the only method of healing is insanity, mere business corruption buying the government overseers whose mission is to protect the public, not sell out to those who endanger the public's health while brainwashing the television audience with lies about drug products that people don't need for diseases or illnesses which are fictional.

There is a "pattern" of corruption involving the hospitals, the medical association, the cancer foundations and the "professional class" that manage the government's "health" regulators. "The revolving door" reality between the career scientists and administrators in government and the private sector (at academic slots or big pharma executive levels) defines corruption, bribery and criminal actions.

A revolution is needed that produces laws guaranteeing "real health care choices" for patients and real competition among vastly different healing therapies. With drug dominance replaced with a greater variety of viable treatments.

Dr. Curt Maxwell Speaks Out

From *The Townsend Letter for Doctors* October 2004

"There are cures for almost every condition and disease. These cures are suppressed. Almost every disease or malady has a business built around it and these businesses actively suppress any solution that would destroy their income base. Drugs cannot cure. They suppress symptoms. All drugs have secondary effects, some life-threatening themselves ... There is no health system in the U.S. It's a farce. It has nothing to do with health.

"The U.S. Medical system has probably the finest emergency medical care in the world and also amazing technologies to diagnose disease but should be considered criminally negligent when it comes to treating degenerate disease.

"The drug pharmaceutical companies control Medicine and direct research. There is no open research. If researchers go "off the path" of researching pharmaceuticals, they are fired and blackballed. The FDA is bought and paid for by the Drug pharmaceutical companies."

Suppression of Natural Medicine

thenaturalguide.com

"*Did you know it's illegal to cure cancer?* Successful alternative treatments for cancer *really* upset the FDA, AMA, American Cancer Society, National Cancer Institute, hospital administrators, technicians, pharmaceutical empires and medical doctors. Conventional cancer treatment is a huge industry that stands to lose billions of dollars when holistic cures work. So when people come up with successful cures, they are hounded by the authorities until they are shut down or thrown in jail.

"... Many holistic physicians believe that cancer is completely reversible through non-toxic treatment. Western allopathic treatments use radiation, chemotherapy and surgery to kill or cut out the pathogen / cancer cells. The result? An immune system seriously compromised or wiped out."

Danger: The 'War on Cancer' Is Failing

by Foster Gamble at website thrivemovement.com

"There are multiple natural treatments that hold enormous potential for curing cancer. Most people haven't heard about them because they were suppressed by those whose money making abilities and control was threatened -- namely the American Medical Association, the FDA, pharmaceuticals, and influential Foundations -- Foundations which get their money from the same people that own the pharmaceuticals.

"The opportunity to spread these treatments far and wide still exists ...

"The treatments include ... Dr. Royal Rife's Frequency Technology.

"... the opportunity remains to replicate his findings and treat millions of people who continue to suffer from cancer."

FORBIDDEN CURES

By Ken Adachi at auricmedia.net

"There are a number of alternative healing therapies that work so well and cost so little ... that Organized Medicine, the Food and Drug Administration and their overlords in the Pharmaceutical Industry (The Big Three) would rather the public not know about them. The reason is obvious.

"The Big Three have collectively engaged in a medical conspiracy ... to influence legislative bodies on both the state and federal level to create regulations that promote the use of drug medicine while simultaneously creating restrictive, controlling mechanisms (licensing, government approval, etc.) designed to limit and stifle the availability of non-drug, alternative modalities.

"In the late '20's and early 1930's, Dr. Royal Raymond Rife from San Diego, California developed a high powered microscope which he used in conjunction with a frequency generator ...

"Rife's microscope was capable of 60,000 magnification! This degree of magnification allowed him to observe LIVE virus and bacteria organisms while he applied the ... resonant frequency from his frequency generator. He was able to destroy all manner of disease organisms (including cancer organisms) by merely tuning the generator to the correct resonant frequency of these organisms."

"Royal Raymond Rife and the Cancer Cure That Worked"

by Barbara Minton

at website tbyil.com (The Best Years in Life)

Excerpts:

"Rife invented a machine that uses a variable frequency, pulsed radio transmitter for producing mechanical resonance in cells. This machine introduced the world to what we now know as *energetic medicine*.

"Rife initially found that he could use specific electro-magnetic frequencies for killing bacteria and viruses without damaging the surrounding tissues. His machine utilized the law of sympathetic resonance.

"The law of sympathetic resonance says if there are two similar objects, and one of them begins to vibrate, the other will begin to vibrate too, even when they are not touching. As an example, think about two identical tuning forks. If you tap either of them, the other will begin to vibrate in sympathy. Here's another example for those who remember Ella Fitzgerald, the amazing singer who could strike a high note and shatter a crystal glass without touching it. The glass shattered because of sympathetic resonance.

"This law was the basis of Rife's ability to destroy disease producing organisms and make those who came to him well again. He viewed each tiny micro-organism as a little tuning fork. He built his Rife Machine to transmit the signal which would make microbes vibrate. By intensifying the signal for distance, he was able to shatter any microbe, just like Ella Fitzgerald's shattered glass.

Royal Rife Announces the Cause of Cancer at a Medical Convention, but Accepts the Political Power of His Opposition and the Long Time Before His Discoveries will Gain its Due Recognition

An excerpt from the *Los Angeles Times* newspaper of May 18, 1940:

Headline: "Powerful Radio Ray Called New Enemy of Cancer Germs"

Germs that cause cancer have been discovered and with a new high-frequency radio "ray" they have been killed in human patients who then recovered, according to assertions made yesterday at the California State Homeopathic Medical Society's convention at Chapman Park Hotel.

The new progress in combating malignant cancer is said to have been made possible by an ultra-microscope that magnifies 31,000 times and by a ray that kills micro-organisms in humans at a distance of 1000 feet.

Both the microscope and the Ray were developed by Royal Raymond Rife of San Diego. He addressed the physicians and showed photographs of the germ which he calls "B.X. filterable virus" of cancer tissue. Rife was to have announced his discovery before the British Medical Society, but made the announcement locally because of the war. (WWII)

Mr. Rife alluded to the fact that the medical profession has not yet accepted his findings and remains skeptical of his microscope.

"My work may not be accepted during my lifetime," he said, "but I can't help that. I know it ultimately will be recognized ... I have made no formal claim that the B.X. virus is the cause of cancer, but I now believe it is the cause. For no less than 104 times this virus has produced tumor in experimental animals without a failure."

"The cancer virus is, I feel sure, the smallest type of organism, measuring only a 20th of a micron. There appear to be only 10 major kinds of organisms, the others evolving from these 10."

Appendix D

Rife Announces That BX Virus Is Cause of Cancer

U.S. Congressman Champions Rife, But FDA Stonewalls

The Mystery Of The Successful Rife Instrument Is Solved

Rife Announces That BX Virus Is Cause of Cancer

Royal R. Rife sent an article to the U.S. cancer experts on cancer in 1954. A committee of the National Research Council and the National Academy of Sciences was formed to evaluate it. They failed to interview Dr. Rife or the doctors who were involved in the clinical trial or any of the patients or all the the prominent scientists who could have corroborated Rife's work. And they refused to even talk to Dr. Rife, let alone view a demonstration of the cancer virus being destroyed by the appropriate "resonant frequency."

Rife's article was titled "History of the Development of a Successful Treatment for Cancer and Other Virus, Bacteria and Fungi." Because of the cancer experts' incompetence, inaction and deliberate bureaucratic obstruction of Rife's discoveries, including opposition to ever testing it honestly, countless cancer patients suffered horribly and unnecessarily, dying of cancer. This perversion of scientific principles and medical ethics can be viewed as the tragic result of medical politics and decades of government cancer policies favoring chemo dogma. Here are selected excerpts from Rife's article:

"After the isolation of the filtered virus and other pathogenic organisms, the idea was conceived, that it would be possible to create an electronic frequency that was in the correct coordination or resonance of the chemical constituents of a given organism or virus, and to devitalize with said frequency, the organism or virus in question.

"The isolation of cancer virus and other micro-organisms was an accomplishment with which I felt a great deal of pride. Finally in 1931, I discovered the transformation of cancer virus and the successful treatment for cancer and other diseases by actual observation of the universal microscope while applying the frequency instrument. Thus, this data is presented for evaluation. With the frequency instrument, no tissue is destroyed, no pain is felt, no noise is audible, and no sensation is noticed. A tube lights up and 3 minutes later the treatment is completed. The virus or bacteria is destroyed and the body then recovers itself naturally from the toxic effect of the virus and or bacteria. Several disease forms may be treated simultaneously.

"... BX virus ... is the primary cause of cancer. We have in our own classification called this virus of cancer -- BX. We do not expect any laboratory to be able to produce BX on account of the technique involved and the lack of adequate optical equipment. The BX or any other virus cannot be seen with the conventional microscope and illuminating systems as we have explained often before. That these tiny live living entities (known as BX virus) cannot be stained with any of the conventional acid or aniline dye stains as they are much smaller in dimension than the molecular particles of said stain and can be seen only by a frequency of light which coordinates with their chemical constituents. All viruses require their own individual frequency of the mono-chromatic beam to make them visible to the human eye.

"We have come to the conclusion that the illuminant in the fields of high powered microscopy is a more important factor than the high power in magnification of the microscope because without this source of illuminant these particles called virus are invisible with any amount of magnification. We have used Koch's postulates in our methods of recovery which are that the organism inoculated into the host must again be recovered in its true form from the host and thus, as stated before this has been repeated hundreds of times proving to our own satisfaction that BX or cancer virus is the cause of malignancy. The BX virus can be readily changed into different forms of its life cycle by the media upon which it is grown."

"The first clinical work on cancer was completed under the supervision of Dr. Milbank Johnson, M.D. which was set up under the special medical Research

Committee at the University of Southern California. Sixteen cases were treated at the clinic for many types of malignancy. After 3 months, 14 of these so-called hopeless cases were signed off as clinically cured by the staff of five medical doctors and Dr. Alvin G. Foord, M.D., Pathologist for the group. The treatment consisted of 3 minutes duration using the frequency instrument which was set on the mortal oscillatory rate for "BX" or cancer (at three days intervals). It was found that the elapsed time between treatments attains better results then cases treated daily. This gives the lymphatic system an opportunity to absorb and cast off a toxic condition which is produced by the devitalized dead particles of the "BX" instrument treatment."

Twenty years before Dr. Rife sent his report to the top cancer experts of the federal government, he completed his marvelous Universal Microscope. It was displayed in 1933 and 1934 in the Fine Art Gallery, Balboa Park in San Diego, California. Newspapers from around the country reported on this masterpiece. A sample description: "The microscopes perfected by Dr. Rife after 18 years of experimentation, accomplished what even most physicists believed was impossible. They magnified to 20,000 or 30,000 times, still preserving the image in its true form and allowing it to be seen with the appearance of depth. They also revealed to the eye unstained cultures through the use of polarized light and a mono-chromatic beam, thus making it possible to study living organisms and those which resisted stain."

Boston's prestigious *Christian Monitor* predicted, "The new, shining instrument is a combination microscope and microspectroscope, and is expected to extend the boundaries of knowledge into new fields, since it is capable of ferreting out objects which hitherto have been invisible to human perception."

Yet the esteemed cancer experts sitting in their elite committees in Washington, D.C. with tons of money for cancer research, couldn't deign to investigate this great pioneer's work, even though he had already demonstrated to the public his awesome creativity.

Another newspaper reported, "Associated with Rife is a corps of scientists and experts in the radio, physics and medical fields. The work to combat man's invisible enemies is coordinated to obtain the highest degee of perfection from each."

Copies of some of the newspaper reports follow.

5, 1933

1933 on display

Outdoor Art Show Opens Thursday

The new Rife universal microscope, invented and manufactured by Dr. Royal R. Rife. The microscope is on display at the Fine Arts gallery.

By OCTAVIE PAGE

Microscope Attracts

The shining universal microscope of Dr. Rife, exhibited in the gallery as "an example of fine and beautiful craftsmanship" has drawn a steady stream of admirers. To some it appears no more than a beautiful but mysterious contraption, but many that we have observed were suffering from a scientist's or student's yearning to get their hands upon it and experiment with its complicated apparatus. However, it is safely protected by glass. Near it a typed legend explains that it magnifies 20,000 times, has 5000 parts, stands 20 inches high, and weighs 200 pounds. The talk which Dr. Rife, its inventor, will give Wednesday, Aug. 9, at 8 p. m., will deal with the theories of microscopic study and the development which has taken place in perfecting the microscope, and in obtaining scientific data therefrom. While the talk is arranged for doctors and other scientists, it is open to all who are particularly interested.

Microscope That Magnifies 20,000 Diameters Exhibited by San Diegan

A new and unique type of microscope, designed and constructed by Royal R. Rife, Point Loma scientist, and including within the single instrument practically all modern systems of microscopy, is on display in Fine Arts gallery, Balboa park.

The apparatus, displayed "as an example of fine and beautiful craftsmanship," magnifies its field to 20,000 diameters. It has 5000 parts, weighs 200 pounds and stands 20 inches high. It is highly polished with a chromium finish—a new departure in Rife microscopes, which until now has been strictly utilitarian instruments with no attempt at beauty of appearance.

Known as the Rife Universal microscope, the instrument can be used with the dark field, nonchromatic and transmitted light, polarized light, opaque illumination, slit ultra-microscope and refractability of crystalography systems of microscopic observation. It is also equipped for micro-photography, and photographs of subjects enlarged 20,000 diameters have been made, according to Rife.

This machine is the third of a series built by Rife for the observation of filterable viruses. Each has embodied refinements and improvements over its predecessor, according to Rife, and the new apparatus eliminates several tedious steps in observation that were required by the older ones. Its construction required nearly five months.

MICROSCOPE MAGNIFIES TO 31,000 TIMES

Dr. R. R. Rife Hopes Invention Will Extend Knowledge; Featured by Variable Prisms

SAN DIEGO, Sept. 22.—(AP)—Dr. Royal R. Rife, with experience gained on the first excursion into a new field of bacteriology, has developed a combination microscope and micro-spectroscope capable of magnifying without diffusion to 31,000 times, which he hopes will extend the boundaries of knowledge still further.

A little more than a year ago the scientist completed in his laboratory here the Rife microscope with a magnification of 20,000 diameters. With it he and Dr. Arthur I. Kendall, prominent Chicago bacteriologist, saw for the first time the filtrable virus of typhoid fever, and, in another experiment conducted in Dr. E. C. Rosenow's laboratory at the Mayo Institute, the hitherto invisible bacilli of infantile paralysis.

UNUSUAL FEATURE

The new instrument, which Dr. Rife called the universal microscope, was constructed on the same principle as the first, making use of the variable, wedge-shaped prisms which were the unusual feature of the Rife microscope.

The microscopes perfected by Dr. Rife after 18 years of experimentation, accomplished what even most physicists believed was impossible. They magnified to 20,000 or 30,000 times, still preserving the image in its true form and allowing it to be seen with the appearance of depth. They also revealed to the eye unstained cultures through the use of polarized light and a monochromatic, variable beam, thus making it possible to study living organisms and those which resisted stain.

Sep 22, 1933 Universal on display

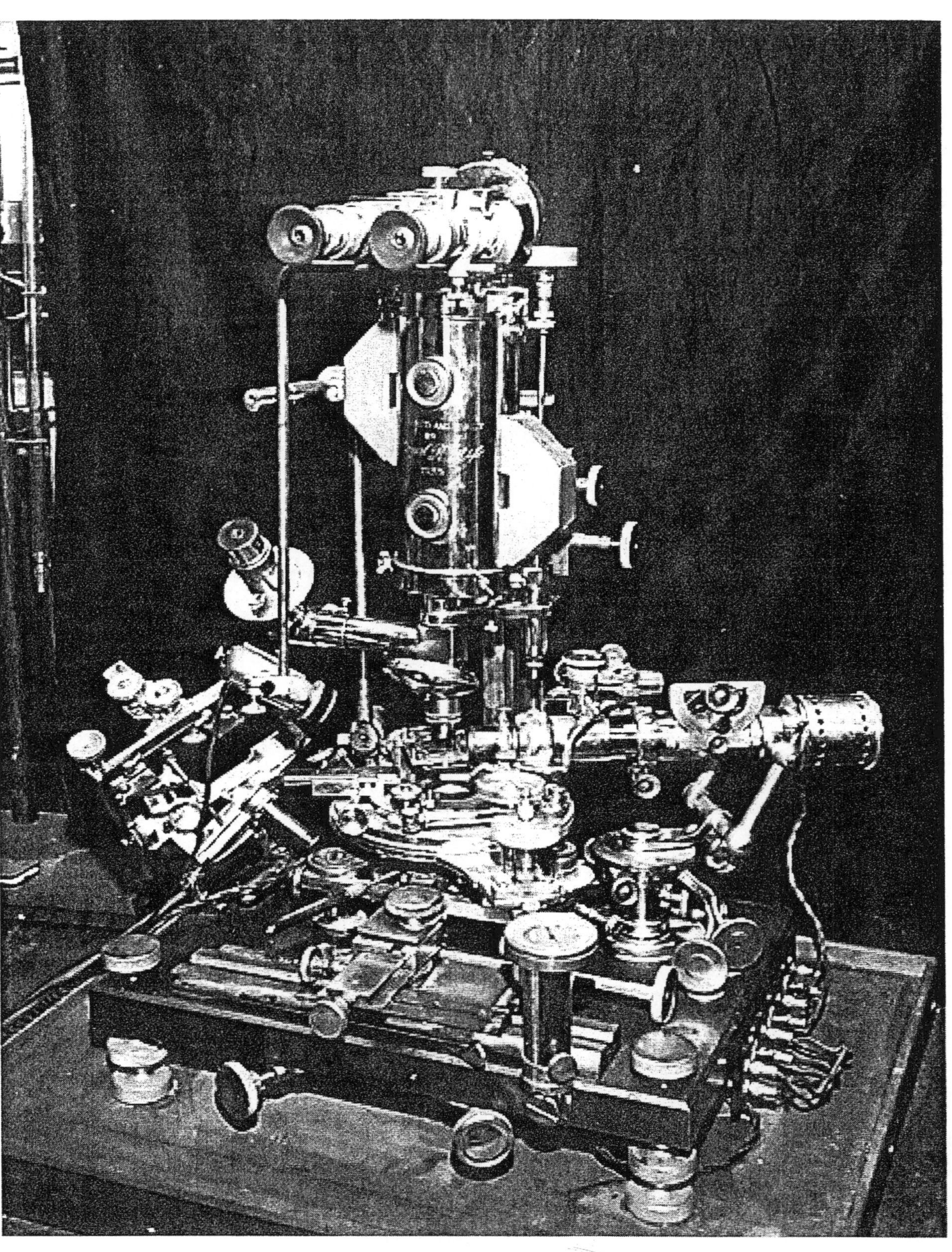

THE CHRISTIAN SCIENCE MONITOR, BOSTON, TUESDAY, APRIL 10, 1934

This Makes Things 31,000 Times as Big

THE CHRISTIAN SCIENCE MONITOR

Dr. Royal R. Rife's Micro-Spectroscope

Common Fly Grows Big as Rooster, Seen By New Microscope

Special to The Christian Science Monitor

SAN DIEGO, Calif.—A new, improved microscope, capable of magnifying without diffusion to 31,000 times, has been perfected here by Dr. Royal R. Rife, natural scientist, and has been on exhibition in the Bridges Fine Art Gallery, Balboa Park.

The new, shining instrument is a combination microscope and microspectroscope, and is expected to extend the boundaries of knowledge into new fields, since it is capable of ferreting out objects which hitherto have been invisible to human perception.

A little more than a year ago in his tiny laboratory above the garage on the estate of the late A. S. Bridges, his benefactor, on Point Loma, Dr. Rife invented a microscope with a magnification of 20,000 diameters. With it, Dr. Rife and Dr. Arthur L. Kendall of Chicago made some astounding discoveries in the realm of physics.

The new instrument, which Dr. Rife calls the universal microscope, was constructed on the same lines as the first, making use of the variable, wedge-shaped prisms which were the unusual feature of the Rife microscope.

S. D. Microscope Magnifies 30,000 Times

By GENE STECK

Following closely his announcement of the discovery of a radio wave germ killer, Royal R. Rife, San Diego scientist, yesterday disclosed scientific developments which have aided him in his intensive laboratory studies of the last four years.

Outstanding are four microscopes, most important of which is the "universal" model. All are constructed on new principals. A "rush order" for one of the "universal" microscopes might be filled in two years, Rife's aids explained. A year or more would be required to make the blueprints alone. There is little likelihood that the microscopes will become as popular as stamp collecting and miniature golf courses—they would cost about a quarter of a millian dollars each.

MANY FILMS OF GERMS

Alice in Wonderland had less to amaze her than a stranger in the Rife laboratory. Rife has recorded on film the life span of many germs. One of the microscopes is equipped with two motion picture cameras and one still camera.

Under extraordinary magnification of the "universal" telescope, a germ has less privacy than the proverbial goldfish. It is scrutinized from all sides and made as transparent as a cellophane wrapper. Magnification is from 10,000 to 30,000 times.

The many adjustments on the microscope make it possible to view the subject from all sides without readjusting the focus, which, at high magnification, could not be regained.

5800 PARTS IN MICROSCOPE

There are 5800 parts in the largest of the four microscopes. Its development parallels in the field of microscopes the advancement expected in telescopic construction when Palomar's 200-inch "eye" is completed.

Associated with Rife is a corps of scientists and experts in the radio, physics and medical fields. The work to combat man's invisible enemies is coordinated to obtain the highest degree of perfection from each.

Although the higher magnifications give excellent definition and clearness, experimental work on viruses has ...

FLY WOULD LOOK LIKE MONSTER UNDER LOCAL SCIENT

Seemingly more complicated than a submarine control room and more interesting than a three-ring circus, Royal R. Rife's "universal" microscope is said to magnify 10,000 to 30,000 times. If it were possible to see a fly thus magnified, it would look like a dinosaurian monster.

CONSTRUCTION INTRICATE

It is difficult for the layman to comprehend Rife's highly technical explanation of the construction of his instrument. He explained that his results were obtained by interposing correcting prisms and blocks of quartz not more than 30 millimeters apart, allowing only a tolerance of less than one wave length of visible light in the core beam of illumination from the objective to the ocular.

By applying this new system ...

discovery of a radio wave germ killer
San Diego Union May 1938

Alice in wonderland had less to amaze her than a stranger in the Rife laboratory.

Associated with Rife is a corps of scientists and experts in the radio, physics and medical fields. The work to combat man's invisible enemies is coordinated to obtain the highest degree of perfection from each.

U.S. Congressman Champions Rife, But FDA Stonewalls

In January 2000 Congressman Cliff Stearns examined the evidence supporting Dr. Royal Rife's scientific research and incredible results in the university-sponsored cancer clinical trial. The congressman was also aware that much open research into frequency medicine was occurring in Europe. But FDA was blocking use of Rife therapies in America.

The congressman was a member of a Health Subcommittee and wanted answers. So he communicated his concern to the Commissioner of the FDA. Including with his letter 8 PAGES of material on Rife's profound breakthroughs along with information on Rife's experience with a numbe of prominent scientists. But it made no difference. Food and Drug Administration functionaries stonewalled the congressman for 3 months.

The congressman wrote another letter, complaining about the way FDA was treating this issue. Still, the congressman got more of the FDA's "wall" treatment. FDA had no intention of doing anything which would threaten the pharmaceutical industry and its expensive monopoly. Copies of both letters by the congressman to the FDA Commissioner are provided in subsequent pages.

The congressman realized that Congress was being deliberately mislead and misinformed about the Rife issue. The FDA would not answer the congressman's reasonable questions about this potential breakthrough using an entirely new method to cure cancer.

Instead, FDA chose to play its familiar game of denial, sending pages of irrelevant registration materials, shifting the topic to side issues that didn't pertain to the congressman's inquiry, and purposely discouraging the congressman by refusing to deal with the science underlining the Rife frequency therapy. Just stalling because FDA wanted to avoid any kind of truth-seeking. Not interested one bit in examining a new treatment for cancer based on a solid, original hypothesis and practical results.

But the congressman called them on their stalling tactics. He thundered, "Do you take me for a fool who can't recognize trite cant?"

The congressman then accused FDA of hypocrisy. He told them they were "ignoring the law ... and endangering the lives of countless Americans with cancer."

Then the congressman questioned whether FDA's "in-house experts have scientific credentials" sufficient to evaluate energy medicine. Thus exposing the great vacuum produced by decades of FDA attacks against Rife's incredible scientific findings. <u>The FDA was out of touch with the reality of Rife's pragmatic medicine.</u>

The congressman declared, "The scientific evidence supporting Rife ... is very impressive. I am appalled that you can assume ... total unawareness when the internet is exploding with reams of information ... Even personnel at the National Cancer Institute are massively downloading Rife files. What gives?"

But FDA refused to have a real discussion and examination of Royal Rife's successful therapy or Rife's hundreds of laboratory tests which confirmed Rife's theory that a microbe was the primary cause of cancer. This has been a taboo topic at the National Cancer Institute and anyone who seeks a cancer-virus linkage has been ostracized.

The congressman told FDA, "There has been no dialogue commenced regarding Rife's cancer curing science when a global internet interest in the subject grows at an accelerating rate ... I just get from you more platitudinous, empty verbiage when real Americans are dying at the rate of 10,000 a week."

Someday there will an accounting because for decades the FDA's "protectors" of the public's health have bowed to the "interests" and let people suffer and die from a disease that could have been cured. Because Dr. Rife had found the cause and learned how to painlessly, non-invasively destroy the causative pathogen -- a virus-sized organism that Rife named BX.

The congressman's final message to FDA will ring for a long time, echoed by many people who know who Royal Rife was and what he did.

These are the congressman's parting words to FDA and its terrible policies and record: "To the degree your agency is arbitrarily ignoring the law and the intent of Congress, as well as endangering the lives of countless Americans with cancer, you are slipping perilously close to bureaucratic tyranny abetted by shameful turf self-interest ... I urge you to trend carefully when the issue is a working, legitimate, easily validated scientific therapy and practice versus FDA regulations which are often reduced to nit-picking."

Is a Committee of Inquiry needed? You bet one would be appropriate if the word "justice" still means anything. Terrible wrongs by corrupt or incompetent government officials can be condemned and corrected. And there are countless future generations that need access to Rife's brilliant "resonant frequency" therapy. Rife's time will come.

CLIFF STEARNS
6TH DISTRICT, FLORIDA

WASHINGTON:
2227 RAYBURN BUILDING
WASHINGTON, DC 20515-0906
(202) 225-5744
FAX: (202) 225-3973
cstearns@mail.house.gov
http://www.house.gov/stearns/welcome.html

Congress of the United States
House of Representatives
Washington, DC 20515-0906

COMMITTEE ON COMMERCE
SUBCOMMITTEES:
ENERGY AND POWER, VICE CHAIRMAN
TELECOMMUNICATIONS, TRADE, AND CONSUMER PROTECTION
HEALTH AND ENVIRONMENT

COMMITTEE ON VETERANS' AFFAIRS
SUBCOMMITTEE:
HEALTH, CHAIRMAN

REPUBLICAN POLICY COMMITTEE

AIR FORCE CAUCUS, CO-CHAIRMAN

January 14, 2000

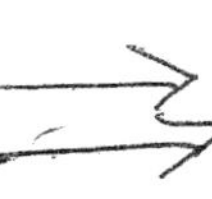

Dr. Jane E. Henney
Commissioner
Food and Drug Administration
5600 Fishers Lane
Rockville, Maryland 20857

Dear Dr. Henney:

This office has received reports that the Food and Drug Administration received extensive information regarding the cancer therapies and scientific discoveries of Royal R. Rife more than 8 years ago but failed to evaluate its potential and proven success.

Given that reports of the Rife therapy's success are now appearing in several places in America and other countries, kindly advise me of your position on Rife therapy and its impact.

It has come to my attention that FDA Consumer magazine has repeatedly denounced or dismissed the Rife therapy. Does your office have information to corroborate this criticism?

In light of the seriousness of cancer, could you provide me with any specific investigation or review that was ever undertaken by your agency on this therapy?

What official in your agency can provide expert testimony on this novel approach to reversing and possibly healing cancer?

Given the seriousness of 10, 000 Americans dying of cancer every week, I believe that the FDA should give consideration to a breakthrough method of cancer therapy-derived from a stunningly original scientific approach. I am concerned that this might not be the case.

The enclosed exhibits, 8 pages, describe what Rife achieved. Please kindly provide a prompt response to the claims made about Rife.

Sincerely,

Cliff Stearns

Cliff Stearns
United States Representative

CS:vtc
Enclosures (8)

bcc: The Honorable William E. Dannemeyer

☐ OCALA
115 S.E. 25TH AVENUE
OCALA, FL 34471
(352) 351-8777

☐ ORANGE PARK
1726 KINGSLEY AVE., #8
ORANGE PARK, FL 32073
(904) 269-3203

☐ LEESBURG
100 S. 11TH STREET, #102
LEESBURG, FL 34748
(352) 326-8285

CLIFF STEARNS
6TH DISTRICT, FLORIDA

WASHINGTON:
2227 RAYBURN BUILDING
WASHINGTON, DC 20515–0906
(202) 225–5744
FAX: (202) 225–3973
cstearns@mail.house.gov
http://www.house.gov/stearns/welcome.html

Congress of the United States
House of Representatives
Washington, DC 20515–0906

COMMITTEE ON COMMERCE
SUBCOMMITTEES:
ENERGY AND POWER, VICE CHAIRMAN
TELECOMMUNICATIONS, TRADE, AND CONSUMER PROTECTION
HEALTH AND ENVIRONMENT

COMMITTEE ON VETERANS' AFFAIRS
SUBCOMMITTEE:
HEALTH, CHAIRMAN

REPUBLICAN POLICY COMMITTEE

AIR FORCE CAUCUS, CO-CHAIRMAN

June 27, 2000

Dr. Jane E. Henney
Commissioner
Food and Drug Administration
5600 Fishers Lane
Rockville, MD 20857

Dear Dr. Henney:

Reference is made to my letters dated January 14, 2000 and March 2, 2000 as well as FDA's late April 2000 response by Ken Mulvy on behalf of Melinda K. Plaisier, Associate Commissioner for Legislation. The material provided included two articles published in FDA CONSUMER. FDA's April 2000 response failed to address my questions relating to the scientific discoveries of Royal R. Rife.

10,000 Americans die of cancer every week while your agency took more than 3 months to reply to my very serious interest in the potential of this Rife cancer therapy. This suggests a fundamental error in FDA's understanding of its obligations and accountability to the American people and America's guiding principles.

There are two key areas of your response to my inquiry that I believe do not adequately answer my questions.

A. You cite the prosecution of a company named REM in Buffalo, N.Y. in the early 1990's and the imprisonment of its officers. A conviction of a company with a pyramid scheme record is not relevant and certainly not germane to the questions I asked your agency to answer.

B. There appear to be serious, factual errors in FDA's published statements concerning Rife's work. This, added to the 3 plus months required to organize your reply, is not entirely acceptable. Furthermore, I wait three months for answers to important questions and receive basic handout material?

Could someone at the Food and Drug Administration now attempt to answer my original questions contained in my inquiry dated January 14, 2000?

Sincerely,

CLIFF STEARNS
United States Representative

CS:vtc

☐ OCALA
115 S.E. 25TH AVENUE
OCALA, FL 34471
(352) 351–8777

☐ ORANGE PARK
1726 KINGSLEY AVE., #8
ORANGE PARK, FL 32073
(904) 269–3203

☐ LEESBURG
100 S. 11TH STREET, #102
LEESBURG, FL 34748
(352) 326–8285

"Your Doctor Can't Cure Your Cancer Because He Can't Prevent or Cure His Own!" **By Dr. Lorraine Day at website DrDay.com**

"Surveys show that 75% of doctors would NOT have chemotherapy if they developed cancer, yet they ... prescribe it for their patients ...

"The U.S. National Institutes of Health (NIH) is arguably the world's foremost medical research center. It is comprised of twenty institutions under one administrative control, including the National Cancer Institute ... The NIH employs more than 18,000 people including thousands of medical researchers on their 70 acre campus in Bethesda, Maryland near Washington, D.C. In 2010, the budget of the NIH was $31 Billion, all from the pockets of hard-working taxpayers.

"Since the NIH was established over 100 years ago, at least $1 trillion have been spent by tens of thousands of scientific researchers to find a cure for cancer and other diseases. But the sad truth is that no cure for ANY disease has ever been found by NIH-funded research, or by any other conventional scientific research organization either.

"Why have they failed so miserably? Because decade after decade they have continued to look in all the wrong places. They have continued to develop more drugs, all of which are harmful and none of which cure disease.

"But I, and thousands of others, are living proof that you CAN get well -- from all disease -- without drugs, including without chemotherapy drugs, without radiation, and without ... surgery."

Dr. Lorraine Day reversed her severe, advanced cancer by rebuilding her immune system by natural therapies, so her body could heal itself. Dr. Day is an internationally acclaimed orthopedic trauma surgeon and best selling author who was for 15 years on the faculty of the University of California, San Francisco School of Medicine.

From "Rife Machine Report" by Jeff Garff:

Available on the independent site Rifevideos.com.

"Rife: 'So we're throwing an electronic frequency through the tissue of the body that simply devitalizes the bacteria with no harm to normal tissue.'

"These statements clearly show again that each organism has its own frequency and that it only takes a single frequency to kill, devitalize or render it harmless.

"This new method that was used to generate the frequencies has been a mystery for the past 75 years. Finally, with the location and purchase of an original Beam Ray Clinical instrument and the use of the spectrum analysis the method ... used has been discovered.

"... it is the only known original ... Beam Ray Clinical instrument to exist ... There were about 14 instruments built by the original Beam Ray Company and until now no one has ever been able to find one. The fact that even one has survived is a miracle.

"It was from the analyzing of this original Beam Ray clinical instrument that the mystery of how it worked was discovered.

"We can conclude that all that is needed is a modulated or pulsed waveform with the proper RF frequency to devitalize microorganisms.

"In summary, with all the historical information that has come to light in the past few years, we finally know the truth about which frequencies were Dr. Rife's M.O.R.s. We also understand the audio frequency sideband spacing method used in the ... Beam Ray Clinical instrument."

Appendix E

Truth Too Dark To Admit

Question

Is the cancer treatment system really this horrible? This corrupt?

Is the racket so deep, so entrenched, so politically protected that any real attempt to eradicate it is hopeless?

If so, then cancer will never be cured. All successful treatment methods will be prohibited or suppressed. Quietly, thoroughly, legally through back room deals and FDA intimidation. A <u>sellout</u> of the public interest.

Because profits, payoffs and future private sector jobs drive the actions of the "professional class" in high government positions, the employees of the phony, ponzi scheme foundations, the government approval committees, the lobbyists, the <u>superficial</u> mainstream medical reporting, and most of the congressional "oversight" prioritites. The "corrupt regulatory practices" will obstruct innovation. Criminal enterprises will thrive while pure science and pure doctoring wither. The simple solution of a national medical freedom law will be opposed.

Massive medical malpractice will continue. A cancer establishment will keep pushing various scientific frauds. All natural therapies will be rejected as "unproven." Deceitful press releases will condemn alternative remedies which have verified clinical success. Unless people denounce the medical racket and the high paid frauds, drug advocates and spin artists at the National Cancer Institute who run the tyranny. And who keep getting the big dollar incentives to maintain the racket.

The NCI directors were all drug dunces, with minds closed to any worthy, non-drug solutions to cancer. Millions died as a result of this treachery. Only a few spoke truth to the false dogma the cancer elite prattled.

She Spoke Truth

Dr. Mahin Khatami is a former project director at the National Cancer Institute (NCI). The following excerpt is from an article published in December 2016:

"War on cancer is a very expensive Government Welfare Program for members of the establishment and their surrogates who enjoy career longevities of 40 - 65 years and who are entitled to continuously receive large sums of travel funds and grants with little / no review processes or producing anything of value to benefit the society.

"... Policy makers in Congress have no clue how to assess worthy or worthless projects as they depend on advice of establishment and their surrogates who occupy high positions ... as the only 'authorities' to defend such illogical projects that are more like 'building bridges to nowhere'

"... independent professional views are perceived as 'threat' to the establishment and professionals become subject to heavy harassment, bullying, unethical and criminal practices of retaliation and elimination."

("NIH Scientist -- Dr Mahin Khatami exposes corruption in cancer and vaccine industries" at Signs of the Times, December 10, 2016, sott.net, which reprints article from *Clinical and Translational Medicine* medical journal, December 2016 issue)

"The Corrupt Politics of Cancer" by Liz Greene, March 17, 2012

website bloomingtonalternative.com

Samuel S. Epstein, M.D. ... has written 270 scientific articles and 18 books on the causes, prevention and politics of cancer ...

In 2008, Harold Varmus, director of the NCi, received a salary of $2.7 million. Varmus eliminated any "price controls on cancer drugs made at the taxpayer's expense," says Epstein ...

The NCI (National Cancer Institute) is rife with conflicts of interest, according to Epstein, and operates a revolving door with polluting and cancer-drug industries.

NCI director from 1981 to 1995, Samuel Broder ... in a 1998 *Washington Post* interview Broder "frankly admitted," Epstein says, "that the NCi has become what amounts to a government pharmaceutical company."

Further, the NCi has blocked funding for research and clinical trials on promising, non toxic, low-cost and unpatentable alternative cancer treatments in favor of highly toxic and sometimes carcinogenic patented cancer drugs developed by Big Pharma, according to Epstein. The NCI backs pharmaceutical companies seeking approval "of their highly touted miracle drugs -- drugs that have shown limited if any success over decades," he asserts.

****

And Congress and the mainstream media ignore these outrages? This criminal collusion? This malfeasance and abandonment of the NCI's mission and purpose to serve the public good in finding a cause and various cures for cancer? To serve instead Big Pharma interests and profits? To maintain a drug monopoly instead of health advocate Sue A. Blevins' "full array of health care choices."

Drug Company Corruption

60 Minutes April 1, 2009 wanttoknow.info

"One of the most expensive bills ever placed before the House of Representatives ... The pharmaceutical lobbyists wrote the bill ... The bill was over a thousand pages ... and we voted for it at about 3 a.m. in the morning ...

"You push this bill through that produces a windfall for the drug companies. And then a short time later, you go to work for the drug lobby at a salary of $2 million ...

"In all, at least 15 congressional and federal officials left to go to work for the pharmaceutical industry, whose profits were increaded by several billion dollars."

Pharmaceutical Industry, AMA, and FDA Endangering Your Health For Profit

Shirley's-Wellness-Cafe.com

"The medical establishment works closely with the drug multinationals whose main objective is profits, and whose worst nightmare would be an epidemic of good health. Lots of drugs must be sold. In order to achieve this, anything goes: lies, fraud and kickbacks ... why do the authorities forbit alternative medicine? Because they are serving the industry ... They control medicine, and that is why they are able to tell medical schools what they can and cannot teach. They have their own set of laws, and they force people into them. That is a mafia."

Guylaine Lanctot, M.D.

<u>Another *60 Minutes* Report -- 5 Years Later</u>

<u>healthimpactnews</u> *60 Minutes* 2014

The CBS News program *60 Minutes* aired an investigative report in 2014 on the scandalous practice of pharmaceutical companies actions with cancer drugs.

Here are some facts about the unethical practice of the drug industry revealed in this report.

Medicare is required by law to pay whatever the drug company charges for their products ... This is due to a law passed a few years ago.

Lesley Stahl: "And there's no negotiating whatsoever with Medicare?"

Doctor: "No."

In addition to this price fixing allowed by law, doctors who prescribe the drugs make a commission on the drugs they prescribe.

Another reason drug prices are so expensive is that according to an independent study, the single biggest source of income for private oncologists is the commission they make from cancer drugs.

The real question is can the current cancer industry really be fixed? While the interview does expose some of the fraud and corruption in the cancer industry, it is still not dealing with the basic issues of how the industry needs sick cancer patients to survive, not cures.

As a result, any treatments for cancer outside of this lucrative pharmaceutical market is aggressively pursued by the FDA and squashed.

****

That's why FDA Commissioners won't respond to inquiries about Royal Rife's cure for cancer. They ignore Congress. They are not working for the public

interest which is their institutional obligation. They serve the drug industry and all those white collar "professional class" managers getting high salaries from government agencies or super salaries, profits and commissions in the private section where the goal is not to find a cure for cancer, but rather to keep "treating" with price-gauging chemo. The "cancer industry" racket is deeply entrenched.

Royal Rife's frequency medicine could destroy the chemo racket.

When Treating Cancer is a Crime

By Dr. Frank Shallenberger

at website secondopinionnewsletter.com

You might remember that California passed a medical freedom bill several years ago. I'm happy to say that this bill has worked out rather well. The medical board is honoring both the letter and spirit of the law. But there was a huge problem with the law -- it completely overlooked cancer treatment.

While the medical board overseas medical treatment, a draconian provision in the Health and Safety Code limits legal treatment for cancer to the foregoing toxic / disfiguring treatments (chemo, radiation, surgery) ... The Department of Health doesn't have to follow the California medical freedom law, so it can turn quite ugly if it chooses to go after those offering non-conventional cancer treatments. It could decide to criminally prosecute a physician for the non-toxic treatment, even if the doctor cures the patient!

"Cash Cow Exposed: The Conspiracy Behind Big Pharma"

By Gregg Prescott, M.S. Holisticcancerresearch.com

"In order to maintain the illusion that cancer can only be treated with surgery, chemotherapy or radiation therapy while being able to pillage the unassuming patient for thousands of dollars, the medical industry and Big Pharma continue to ignore alternative medicine and proven cures.

"Gwen Olson ... worked as a pharmaceutical sales representative for 15 years ... Gwen stated, 'We were being trained to misinform people ... I started to realize that these patients were literally being tortured by the drugs that they were given!

" 'There is no theory behind what I am telling you,' stated Olson. 'It is all provable. And what I am saying is provable is that the pharmaceutical industry doesn't want to cure people!'

"Gwen is the author of *Rx Drug Pusher*.

"Dr. Royal Rife, a microbiologist, was reverting cancer cells into normal cells in the 1930s, long before the discovery of DNA."

"History of Alternative Cancer Treatment (2)" by Gavin Phillips from website healingcancernaturally.com

Excerpt:

"The supposed 'war on cancer' is little more than a grand illusion conjured up by the cancer establishment's propaganda gurus. The formula is eons old. Repeatedly chisel your message into people's psyches, 'cancer breakthroughs' ... 'Turning the tide on cancer' ...

"There never was a determined, no-holds-barred war on cancer. There is a fanatical and hate-filled war being waged against the few courageous doctors and innovating healers who prescribe natural treatments. There is a war of protectionism. Protecting the status quo, protecting the great money trough, and above all protecting the pharmaceutical cartel's monopoly. There have been at least a dozen very encouraging cancer treatments in the last seventy years ... They all have two things in common. The people advocating the therapy are branded charlatans or quacks and the treatment has been denounced as worthless by scientists who have been selling out for generations.

"A radical change in cancer research is needed. The natural, nutritional and other innovative approaches should be studied and made available to cancer patients immediately. Most important, we must have medical freedom of choice."

DARKNESS AT NOON: THE EXPERTS LIED AND STILL ARE LYING

The entire "cancer industry" is fundamentally corrupt. It needs a top-to-bottom overhaul. Chemo's effectiveness is a lie. Academia sold out to the drug cartels many decades ago. Rife's wonderful discoveries could have revolutionalized health care. His therapy was suppressed. The entire society was told that only "conventional medicine" was science-based -- a monstrous fiction by the cancer establishment and its elite "authorities."

From an article titled "Exposing the Fraud And Mythology of Conventional Cancer Treatments" at cureyourowncancer.org:

"The treatment of cancer in the U.S. is one of the most bald-faced cover-ups in medical history ... You deserve to know the truth about the criminality of oncologists and about the dangers of chemotherapy, conventional cancer treatments and the cancer 'business.' "

From an article titled "The Cancer Industry Is Too Prosperous to Allow a Cure" by John Thomas, at healthimpactnews.com:

"The research dollars have all been devoured by a cancer monopoly -- a cartel -- consisting of pharmaceutical companies, the American Medical Association, a research system that supports pharmaceutical manufacturers, a system of charities that raise money for cancer research, and various federal agencies such as the US FDA. These groups have little interest in curing cancer, but are fully committed to earning profits for the cancer monopoly that is headed by the pharmaceutical companies ...

"There is a revolving door of pharmaceutical industry representatives who hold influential positions in these agencies having strong ties to their former (and future) pharmaceutical employers ... Thus, the principle of overseeing public safety and efficacy has been replaced by the profit motivation of the pharmaceutical industry. These agencies not only serve the cartel and the cancer factory but they are working to prevent anyone who is not part of the cartel from successfully introducing alternative cancer treatments into the medical care system."

From "How Cancer Politics Have Kept You in the Dark Regarding Successful Alternatives" by W. John Diamond and W. Lee Cowden

"The reason alternative cancer treatments are not mainstream has little to do with alleged therapeutic ineffectiveness and far more to do with political control over the therapy marketplace ... The doctors who perform cancer treatments and the scientists who conduct research are not the ones in control of the cancer field. It is the larger power structure of the cancer establishment that effectively controls the shape and direction of cancer prevention, diagnosis, and treatment. The field of U.S. cancer care is organized around a medical monopoly that insures a continuous flow of money to the pharmaceutical companies, medical technology firms, research institutions, and government agencies such as the Food and Drug Administration (FDA) and the National Cancer Institute (NCI) and quasi-public organizations such as the American Cancer Society (ACS).

"This is the "cancer industry," says Ralph Moss, Ph.D.

FDA uses mafia tactics for the benefit of Big Pharma

by Jon Rappoport at soft.net on June 22, 2014

Here's the story:

In a stunning interview with Truthout's Martha Rosenberg, former FDA drug reviewer Ronald Kavanaugh exposes the FDA as a relentless criminal mafia protecting its client Big Pharma with a host of mob strategies.

Kavanaugh: "... widespread racketeering, including witness tampering and witness retaliation."

"I was threatened with prison."

"One (FDA) manager threatened my children ... I was afraid I could be killed for talking to Congress and criminal investigators."

We are not dealing with isolated incidents of cheating and lying. We are not dealing with a few isolated bought-off FDA employees. The situation at the FDA isn't correctable with a few firings. This is an ongoing criminal enterprise, and any government official, serving in any capacity who has become aware of it and has not taken action, is an accessory to mass poisoning of the population.

"FDA Death Meter"

By ANH-USA July 5, 2016 Anh-usa.org

How many deaths is the FDA responsible for?

The US Food and Drug Administration (FDA) is responsible for all of the following:

* Approving unsafe drugs that kill hundreds of thousands of people and make millions more sick.

* Endlessly delaying approval for innovative therapies that have long since been approved in Europe and Japan, and which have an excellent safety profile and record, presumably to protect the monopoly position of existing therapies.

* Eliminating and restricting consumer access to natural treatments -- also presumably linked to protecting the monopoly position of drug companies.

... many Americans are unaware of the full extent of the harm caused by this agency that seems deeply mired in corruption.

At ANH-USA, we've worked to expose the corruption of the FDA and fight back against its vendetta against natural medicine.

"FDA's Own Scientists Describe Intimidation Of Big Pharma"

From Dr. Betty Martini, D. Hum. July 23, 2006 rense.com

"FDA's own scientists report pattern of intimidation, censorship and scientific fraud that undermines public safety.

... the Food and Drug Administration's own scientists describe the agency as an environment of intimidation, censorship and scientific fraud. A summary of 997 FDA scientists revealed that forty percent feared 'retaliation' for voicing safety concerns over prescription drugs in public. Over one-third of the scientists didn't even feel safe expressing safety concerns inside the agency, behind the closed doors!

"Intimidation and censorship have been well documented at the FDA and this survey adds further weight to the evidence that the FDA has been utterly co-opted by the pharmaceutical industry and now serves Big Pharma's commercial interests rather than anything resembling a commitment to honest science or public safety.

"In this environment of such scientific fraud, reported first-hand by FDA scientists, to imagine that our system of drug approval has anything to do with 'evidence-based medicine' is nothing short of preposterous. All the billions of dollars in advertising, propaganda, donations to politicians and bribing of doctors can't cover up the sobering truth: The drug industry today is a massive criminal enterprise operating in broad daylight, and the FDA is its chief enforcer. It has nothing to do with honesty, integrity or even health, but everything to do with generating obscene profits, exploiting patients and controlling information through intimidation.

"American Cancer Society: The World's Wealthiest 'Nonprofit' Institution is Losing the War on Cancer" by Samuel S. Epstein, M.D.

"Of the members of the ACS board, about half are clinicians, oncologists, surgeons, radiologists and basic molecular scientists -- and most are closely tied in with the NCI ... In this private club, easy access to funding is one of the 'perks,' and the board routinely rubber-stamps approvals. A significant amount of ACS research funding goes to this extended membership. Such conflicts of interest are evident in many ACS priorities ..."

"The Truth About American Cancer Society"

By Pat Wick **chondrosarcoma.org** **April 13, 2010**

"Tax records show from 2003 to 2006, (American Cancer) Society contributions totalled 3.77 billion; and when you figure nearly 50 percent of that went to salaries, benefits and payroll taxes, the numbers just don't add up as any great effort to cure cancer.

"A full page in the New York Times last June (2009) says both the National Cancer Institute and the American Cancer Society are 'playing it safe in Cancer Research.' "

"Thoughts on American Cancer Society. You Make Me Want to Vomit. So Does Your CEO and His 16 Million Dollar Retirement Package"

rockstarronan.com **February 12, 2013**

"This is just sick! Lining their own pockets on the backs of those suffering with cancer, and begging for more and more money to do it. Terrible."

"How American Cancer Society Uses Your Money"

By David M. Schwartz at website Gothamgr.com

"It's time to look at what the American Cancer Society does with the ONE BILLION DOLLARS you spend every year, money that is given to you by very hard working people ... People of the United States think that you spend the money on the curing, treatment and prevention of cancer, when in reality these contributions fund high overhead, excessive salaries, high expenses, excessive reserves of assets and contributions to political parties.

"The above list barely scratches the surface of a clear mission to pad the pockets of this organization's management and other 'friends' rather than treatment and prevention of cancer.

"... ACS has turned its back on innocative cancer therapies and, instead, pushes, as hard as it can, the cancer drugs manufactured by the very same companies that ACS is in bed with ... and from whom the ACS receives millions of dollars of funding. ACS has also showed that it will destroy the reputations of doctors who try to recommend alternative treatments as opposed to the drugs made by ACS's preferred manufacturers."

Ah, The Cancer Racket. It's Such A Sweet Life

"American Cancer Society (ACS)" Truthwiki.org

"Former CEO John R. Seffrin received $2.4 million salary / compensation from the 'charity' for 2009-2010 fiscal year ... These big organizations, non-profit or not, seem to be ponzi schemes set up to look like a 'war on cancer' when in fact they have corporate sponsors who manufacture, process, distribute and sell cancer-causing foods ...

"People need to realize these huge corporations in sheep's clothing are not seeking the cure for cancer but rather running a cut-throat business.

"One way to help the cancer drug industry remain 'in control' of chemical cancer treatments as the mainstream method for treating cancer is to aggressively attack any competition they may have, including holistic and natural treatments for cancer ... ACS has a track record of keeping records of alternative cancer treatments they criticize."

"Most Censored Story: Does The American Cancer Society Work To Prevent Cancer?"

democracynow.org April 13, 2000

"Project Censored handed out awards to journalists, academics and activists for covering stories that have been censored by mainstream media. Among them was Dr. Samuel Epstein ... He exposed the American Cancer Society ... It gets money from surgeons, from drug companies, from corporations, that he says profit from the cancer industry and have little interest in cancer prevention. According to Dr. Epstein, the American Cancer Society spends most of its money on overhead, salaries and fringe benefits, little on cancer prevention."

"Is Your Favorite Charity Paying For A CEO's Mansion?"

By Andrew Meyer wearechange.org December 6, 2013

"In 2009, the American Cancer Society (ACS) spent $149 million on cancer research after raising over $455 million in Relay for Life events. They spent over $499 million on salary, employment benefits, payroll taxes and another $152 million on supplies, telephone bills, postage, shipping, meetings and travel expenses.

"Even more disturbing, ACS repeatedly has close financial ties to the makers of mammography equipment and cancer drugs. They also receive financial support from the pesticide, petrochemical, biotech, cosmetics, and junk food industries -- products which are primary contributors to cancer.

"ACS's board of trustees has even included an executive from the American Cyanamid Company which makes chemical fertilizers and herbicides before producing anti-cancer drugs. On the receiving end of cancer research money, researchers have been frequently caught fabricating positive findings with the end goal of producing more drugs."

Oh The Corruption

From "The American Cancer Society Runs With the Money and Away From the Cure" by Tony Isaacs. From a 2010 article.

"The American Cancer Society has ... huge cash revenues, land holdings and other assets, and salaries that range to above a million dollars for top executives as well as company automobiles and generous benefits.

"... the 'Chronicle of Philanthropy' reported that the American Cancer Society was more interested in accumulating wealth than saving lives ... By 2009, net assets on hand ... over $1.3 billion.

"The ACS's far-flung and aggressive fund raising appeals routinely plead poverty and tell us that the ACS needs more funds to support its cancer program. However, all the while the American Cancer Society holds over a billion dollars in cash, investments and real estate assets."

Now does the reader begin to understand why Royal Rife's discovery that led to a cure for cancer and other diseases was such a threat to so many and had to be denounced while the cancer industrial complex endorsed expensive orthodox treatments?

From John Diamond, M.D. and Lee Cowden, M.D. comes a stark, awful reminder of what is really at work here. (Healingcancernaturally.com)

"To the cancer establishment, a cancer patient is a profit center. The actual clinical and scientific evidence does not support the claims of the cancer industry. Conventional cancer treatments are in place as the law of the land because they pay, not heal, the best. Decades of the politics-of-cancer-as-usual have kept you from knowing this, and will continue to do so until you wake up to this reality."

CHEMOTHERAPY KILLS

"Study accidently exposes chemotherapy as fraud -- tumors grow faster after chemo"

By Jonathan Benson naturalnews.com January 2013

"A team of researchers from Washington state ... accidentally uncovered the deadly truth about chemotherapy ...

" You might call it the "smoking gun" that proves, once and for all, the complete fraud of the conventional cancer industry. Not only is chemotherapy, the standard method of cancer treatment today, a complete flop, based on the findings, but it is actually detrimental for patients with cancer. Published in the journal *Natural Medicine*, the shock findings which, not surprisingly, are being ignored by the mainstream scientific community, highlights in full detail how chemotherapy causes healthy cells to release a protein that actually feeds cancer cells and causes them to thrive and proliferate ...

"What this means, for all intents and purposes, is that the entire process of chemotherapy is completely worthless ..."

****

It is really a vast conspiracy of the major medical and science "professionals" who stay silent in order to avoid being ostracized and to advance their own interests. It's a sellout of the cancer patients and the public's health. The conspiracy is deep and wide, having been in place for many decades, with the management class at the government's health agencies especially at fault. The appointed heads and top staff at the National Cancer Institute (NCI), the Food and Drug Administration (FDA), and the Department of Health and Human Services have demonstrated extraordinary negligence through

ignoring the poisonous situation and/or whitewashing the deceit perpetrated against the public interest. <u>But the "revolving door" requires they adhere to the politics or they don't get those high-fee jobs when they leave government service for their private sector "payoff."</u>

TOP DOCTORS: CHEMOTHERAPY ONE OF DOZENS OF PROCEDURES SHOWN TO 'GIVE NO BENEFIT'

By Vicki Batts **fourwinds10.com** **October 2016**

"Chemotherapy is arguably one of the medical industry's biggest frauds. Perhaps that's why it recently landed on a list of ineffectual treatments drawn up by the Academy of Medical Royal Colleges (AMRC) ...

"The list was created by 11 top specialists who were each asked to think of five treatments they felt provided little or no patient benefit.

" 'The treatment is by its very nature toxic,' the college said. 'Therefore, the combition of failing to achieve a response and causing toxicity can do more harm than good.'

"Research has shown that in some hospitals up to 50 percent of cancer patients are dying not from the disease, but from chemotherapy drugs. For the first time ever, researchers actually looked at the number of patients who were dying within 30 days of chemotherapy administration, which could indicate that the treatment was the cause of death rather than the cancer. What they found was horrifying."

****

Odd. The scientific and medical professionals never examined those "numbers." With all those billions of dollars spent on research since the beginning of the "War on Cancer" in 1971, no one wanted to find out the % of patients who died after receiving chemotherapy. How convenient. Yet people still claim that protecting chemo and preventing the use of any "alternative therapies" weren't imperatives for the drug industry and the government agencies "protecting the public's health." There are times when business practices and agency "turf" decisions can become criminal activities. All those "nods and winks" and the avoidance of what would be ethically correct -- condemning these crimes.

Appendix F

In the Public Interest?

The Doctor's Oath: First, Do No Harm?

***Primum non nocere* is a Latin phrase that means, "first, do no harm." ... one of the principal precepts of bioethics that all American healthcare students are taught in school and is a fundamental principle throughout the world. (Wikipedia)**

Members of the U.S. Congress often talk about "innovative therapies" when they are holding hearings related to matters involving the Department of Health and Human Services (HHS). "Exciting innovations" in 2017 lingo.

Yet few in the U.S. Congress are even aware of what Royal Rife did in the 1930s with his "innovative therapies." Curing cancer. Curing tuberculosis. Curing cataracts. And lots more. Even incurable conditions, deadly diseases and "undiagnosed" maladies.

There is something suspicious with the U.S. Congress being so uninformed about a story that countless Americans have become aware of since 1987 when the Rife book exploded into the American and the world's consciousness. The story of Rife's comet blaze across the science heavens.

Why can't "frequency medicine" get a little help from those who were elected by the American people to guarantee the quality of the public health system? Rife's breakthrough therapy could have been "scaled up" rapidly from successful "small model" trials. It wasn't. It was fought aggressively and criminally by established interests. The federal "health" agencies couldn't (officially) "find" it even when people at the National Cancer Institute were massively downloading "Rife material" from the internet!

When future American societies have medical facilities filled with all kinds of advanced frequency devices -- as they will -- they will surely look back and condemn the ineptness of the U.S. Congress as well as the executive branch "health" institutions for what was unconscionable conduct by legislative overseers and medical bosses. For fumbling or obstructing the mainstreaming of Royal Rife's contribution in enhancing every human's health in every country and region on this earth.

Excerpts from *The End of Illness* by Dr David Agus:

"The truth is that some doctors inflict a lot of harm today. The entire notion of 'do no harm' has been corrupted; we've moved to an extreme place in medicine that's rarely data-driven and is horrendously overrun by false or unproven claims. And that's scary." (pages 4-5)

"I am an oncologist who cannot treat advanced cancer well. Medical science has made extraordinary progress over the past century, but in my field, the progress stalled out years ago." (page 6)

"... We haven't found many new pills lately that really cure diseases. This is why the pharmaceutical industry is somewhat broken right now ... We need a different approach -- a new model."

(The following quotations from *The End of Illness* were selected by Yeong Sek Yee and Khadijah Shaari for a book review. cancercaremalaysia.com.)

"5 Cancer Facts That Big Pharma Is Now Aggressively Claiming Are Myths" by Dave Mihalovic at website realfarmacy.com

"Doctors and pharmaceutical companies make money from it. That's the only reason chemotherapy is still used. Not because it's effective, decreases morbidity, mortality or diminish any specific cancer rates. In fact, it does the opposite. Chemotherapy boosts cancer growth and long term mortality rates ... It destroys the immune system.

"The cancer industry could never show the public the true 97% statistical failure rate in treating long-term metastic cancers ... it would be very clear to the world that chemotherapy makes little or no contribution to cancer survival at all.

"Money, greed and profits run the cancer industry -- nothing else. The cancer establishment must retreat from the truth to treat cancer because there will never be any profit for them in eradicating the disease."

"Big Pharma -- The History of Pharmaceutical Companies"

(Pharma -- Cartel)

By Shelley Belcourt at website shelleybelcourt.com

"Since the marketplace for the pharmaceutical investment business depends upon the continued existence of diseases, the drugs it developed were not intended to prevent, cure or eradicate disease. Thus, the goal of the global strategy was to monopolize health for billions of people with pills that nearly cover symptoms but hardly ever address the root cause of disease. The deprivation of billions of people from having access to life saving information about the health benefits of natural health approaches, whilst at the same time establishing a monopoly with largely ineffective and frequently toxic patented drugs, caused disease and death in genocidal proportions.

"This epidemic of unnecessary disability and death by the pharmaceutical business with disease is unparalleled in history.

"Linus Pauling and other eminent scientists deserve credit for having kept open the door of knowledge about the health benefit of vitamins and other effective natural health approaches. If it were not for them we would already be living in a health prison today, guarded by the gatekeepers of the pharmaceutical business ..."

Excerpts from the Introduction to

***Cancer Cures and Cover Ups: Political and Economic Corruption of Healthcare* by Mark Porringa, 2006. Entire Introduction available at holimedex.com**

"... conventional treatments are encountering escalating opposition from a growing chorus of informed critics advocating a more holistic approach that actually addresses the causes of cancer, rather than merely suppressing the symptoms at great expense. Sadly, cancer research and its treatment using chemo, radiation and surgery has become a very lucrative business despite the dismal success rate ...

"... independent researchers backed with copious amounts of practical 'living proof' evidence of the therapeutic value of their diverse treatment methods are routinely harassed and persecuted into obscurity for daring to question this arrogant, power mongering white elephant that has driven healthcare costs through the stratosphere. Numerous promising cures continue to be actively suppressed to protect the vested interests of various branches of the medical monopoly, including its regulators which all appear to be in bed together in this conspiracy of suppression and silence ...

"The existing approach of continuing with long term dependence on costly artificial drugs with all their indeterminate and frequently fatal side effects must be stopped if our health care system is to return to some measure of sanity.

"Ultimately, the real blame for this horrendous miscarriage of professional ethics rests almost entirely with the upper level power brokers who perpetuate the symptomatic focus of modern medicine for entirely selfish reasons, using corrupt regulatory practices to advance their monopolistic purposes, fleecing the public with exhorbitant healthcare costs and providing woefully inadequate services all the while padding their bank vaults with obscene levels of 'ill gotten gain'.

"... It is an absolute travesty that so called democratic nations priding themselves on freedom, that totalitarian agencies such as these can prevent terminally ill cancer patients from even accessing information, let alone electing for treatments of their own choice."

"Making A Killing With Cancer: A 124.6 Billion Dollar Industry"

theorganicpepper.ca

"Don't let all the media hype about 'The Cure' fool you. No one who is in a position to do so wants to end cancer because they are all making a killing on the big business of treatment, while ordinary people go broke, suffer horribly, and die.

"There will never be a 'cure' brought to market because there just isn't enough profit in eradicating the disease entirely. There will never be a governing body that protects consumers from being subjected to known carcinogens, because that too, will stop the cash from rolling in. A great deal of research is covered up and many potential cures are ignored and discredited ..."

"The Mind Of James Donahue" at website perdurabo10.net

"Cancer ... A cure for the disease appears to have been known since 1934 and has been kept under wraps, by court order, ever since.

"There is an amazing story behind the discovery. It involved a genius named Royal Rife (1888-1971) who invented the first microscope powerful enough to see and identify bacteria and virus, used it to identify two types of virus that he said caused cancer, and then involved a sound frequency machine that destroyed them.

"Rife claimed the device not only stopped cancer, it also destroyed herpes, polio, spinal meningitis, tuberculosis, tetanus and over 50 other dangerous disease-causing organisms. He literally invented a machine that would cure the ills of everyone. All it took was someone trained to find and identify the virus ... set the correct resonance, and zap it.

"Sometime in recent years an original Rife resonator machine was found intact. It was secretly studied, modified and information about how to build it began circulating on the World Wide Web.

"We hear through informed sources ... that research is currently underway at a major medical instrument company to develop an even better Rife sound resonator machine. If the AMA doesn't block it, the machine may soon be available to doctors everywhere."

"The Cancer Industry: Failure, Lies And Big Profits"

By Paul Fassa March 2, 2014 at website alignlife.com

"If you or someone you love is diagnosed with cancer, it is in your best interest to consider a second opinion away from the mainstream of the cancer industry. Oncologists will insist and even demand your immediate acceptance of surgery, radiation and / or chemotherapy. They will frighten you more than you already are with all kinds of horror tales and statistical babble ...

"Consider the statement written by the past president of the American Chemical Society, Alan C. Nixon: 'It is incomprehensible to me that physicians can ignore the clear evidence that chemotherapy does much, much more harm than good' ...

"Cancer researcher and founder of the University of Michigan's Comprehensive Cancer Center, Max Wicha, was interviewed by the *Pittsburgh-Post Gazette* health section not long ago and delivered the bombshell, 'Standard cancer treatments not only fail to eradicate cancer, but make it worse.'

"It's no surprise that the war on cancer has created huge revenues for all the cancer foundations and their employees as well as the major pharmaceutical companies, medical equipment manufacturers, hospitals and oncologists. Yet there is no healing for cancer with mainstream medicine. Healing only exists outside of mainstream medicine, and effective therapies are maligned and suppressed by the AMA and FDA with help from the media outlets that benefit from the Medical Mafia's advertising revenue.

"John D. Rockefeller financed the rise and dominance of allopathic medicine over all other forms. He was more concerned with his huge financial stakes ... in the burgeoning pharmaceutical industry, rather than public health ...

"The cancer industry suppresses the overwhelmingly empirical and laboratory evidence of alternative natural cancer treatments ... any health practitioner or MD who uses truly effective alternative methods that are inexpensive and without serious side effects is hounded out of practice or worse. And that's one reason why you don't know much about these alternatives."

A Medical Nuremberg

By Patrick Rattigan, N.D. from his article "The Cancer Business"

at website theforbiddenknowledge.com

"While these doctors, nurses etc., involved in the carnage have, through fear, ignorance or finance, kept their heads well down, there have been some honest observers who have taken a stand ...

"Medical Malpractice is defined in the Gould Medical Dictionary as 'improper or injurious medical or surgical treatment through carelessness, ignorance or intent' ... another authority goes further ... 'A more serious criminal lack of care arising from deliberate disregard for the care and safety of other persons constitutes manslaughter' " (B.A. Richards, *Topic of Cancer*)

"The old idea that a doctor should 'first do no harm' has been forgotten ... No wonder the public is beginning to revolt against such barbarous treatment." (Dr Alec Forbes)

"There will be a medical edition of the Nuremberg trials. The atrocities now being committed in the name of orthodox medicine, the suppression of life-giving data, the needless loss of lives, mutilation of bodies and excessive suffering will not continue to be tolerated ... ultimately these criminals and their political lackeys will be brought to trial." (Dr Bruce Halstead)

"Oncologists and Chemo"

at website inspire.com

"Surveys of oncologists by the *Los Angeles Times* and the McGill Cancer Center in Montreal shows that from 75% to 91% of oncologists would refuse chemotherapy as a treatment for themselves or their families. Why? Too toxic and not effective. Yet, 75% of cancer patients are urged to take chemo by their oncologists."

"Cancer Docs Profit From Chemotherapy Drugs"

By Rehema Ellis of NBC News at website Quora.com

"It is a unique situation in medicine: Unlike other kinds of doctors, cancer doctors are allowed to profit from the sale of chemotherapy ...

"Doctors in other specialties simply write prescriptions. But oncologists make most of their money by buying drugs wholesale and selling them to patients at marked up prices."

The "Public Interest" Was Sacrificed for the Doctors' Wallets

When the government's regulatory or "oversight" agencies and the U.S. Congress both conspire with the pharmaceutical cartel, the public health is wrecked. It isn't a "free market" bringing dynamic progress, as the Big Pharma shills propogate, it's corruption mauling the public interest. The following excerpt is from a review of Marcia Angell's book *The Truth About Drug Companies*. It puts a spotlight on big pharma's lobbying malfeasance.

"Health Corruption" from Wanttoknow.info, October 7, 2004:

"The most recent and perplexing lobbying effect caused Congress explicitly to prohibit Medicare from using its huge purchasing power to get lower prices for drugs, thus opening up a dollar pipeline in the form of higher drug prices, directly from taxpayers to corporate coffers. These changes, along with the cave-in by the Food and Drug Administration (FDA) in 1997 that permitted direct-to-consumer advertising to bypass mention in their ads of all but the most serious side effects has further augmented profits. The overall effect has been a corruption not only of science but also of the dissemination of science."

The Alliance for Human Research Protection (AHRP) in reviewing the same book from the former editor of America's most prestigious medical journal, asserted:

"*The Truth About Drug Companies* (2004), an influential book by Marcia

Angell, M.D., who had been editor of the *New England Journal of Medicine* for two decades, laid bare the ubiquitious influence industry has on medicine.

"... those most responsible for the corruption of medicine are medicine's academic leaders, prestigious medical institutions, journal editors, experts charged with formulating practice guidelines, and federal oversight agencies.

"When academia and government agencies become stakeholders in the business of medicine, promoting the commercial interests of manufacturers, rather than the public interest, they betray the public trust and their professional integrity."

("Medical Journals Complicit in Corruption of Medicine")

****

"The problem with doctors starts with their education. The whole system is paid for by the drug industry from education to research. The drug industry has bought the minds of the medical profession, and it starts the day you enter medical school. All the way through, everything is supported by the drug industry."

(T. Collin Campbell, "Corruption in Our Medical System," CANCER COMPASS -- AN ALTERNATE ROUTE, cancercompassalternateroute.com)

"The Cancer Treatment Protection Racket" by John Smith

energygrid.com April 2012

... chemotherapy and radiotherapy, the two cornerstones of modern orthodox cancer treatment are not effective treatments to the vast majority of cancer patients, and yet these "treatments" are given protected monopoly status by most developed countries around the world, effectively sentencing 96% - 98% of cancer sufferers to hugely destructive and painful treatments which are not to their benefit.

So going back to cancer treatment, we see an insanely conventional cancer treatment industry not only ineffective for the vast majority of cancer sufferers and based mostly on spurious science, but one that has also been granted a monopoly by our governments to prevent other treatments ... from even being discussed ... The situation cannot be, by any stretch of the imagination, in the public interest.

... the whole edifice of modern cancer care is rotten at the core because policy is controlled by big business.

Whatever happened to the doctor's oath of "First, Do No Harm?"

Whatever happened to objective testing of medical breakthroughs such as Royal Rife finding a micro-organism of virus size that caused cancer and could be easily eliminated through the use of "resonant frequency" therapies?

The "Cancer Establishment" Condemns Royal Rife

Alas, the cancer "authorities" who determined the American government's cancer priorities and policies, did not want anything to do with Dr. Rife's laboratory findings, his breakthrough in optics and the physics of light, and certainly not his clinical success in healing cancer and other diseases by destroying their virus cause.

Instead, they wanted to maintain their power, their high paid incomes along with all the accompanying goodies, conventions, prestige, published papers in prominent medical and scientific journals, and especially their tyranny of experts status as the spokespeople of standards and the accepted <u>dogma</u>. Their cruel monopoly was imposed on the unsuspecting people of America who trusted them, who wrongly believed the cancer experts weren't self-serving idiots and sell-outs with closed minds to the new, even if hard evidence supported an elegant original theory.

"Objective scientific evaluation" was preached, but the reality was very different. The big money went into research by the "credentialed elite." Compared to Dr. Rife, they were mostly incompetent amateurs. Many <u>hundreds of millions of cancer patients</u> suffered horribly and died because they were not allowed access to what could heal them -- as the doctors who worked with Royal Rife confirmed again and again. Only to suffer the wrath of a corrupt AMA boss and many private and public cancer institutions that abused their responsibility and funding.

Dr. Rife's careful science was never tested by the "authorities."

It was attacked viciously and ignorantly by the American Medical Association, the American Cancer Society, the National Cancer Institute, the Food and Drug Administration, Big Pharma profiteers and all those defending and benefitting from the funds sloshing through the hands of those who were the "Cancer Establishment."

A new look at Dr. Rife's findings are long overdue -- for the sake of generations still unborn who might finally benefit from this man's dedication and genius.

* * * * * *

"Perhaps the greatest irony is that the actual data shows that orthodox methods not only do not work, but they hasten the deaths of the patients, causing agonizing pain and suffering while making huge sums of money for the racket. Radiation, surgery, and chemotherapy are spectacular failures, 'proven' only in fantasy, while methods that are vastly more effective, and also cheap and harmless, are banned for being 'unproven.' The great fear of the people running the racket is the appearance of an actual cure, because then the game would be over."

The Medical Racket by Wade Frazier, June 2014

Oh-Oh! San Diego Newspaper Breaks The Censorship on Rife. The Story of Roy Rife's Successful Cancer Clinical Trial Reaches 21st Century Public. The Medical Establishment Is Not Happy.

All the major newspapers were afraid to tell the Rife story. Afraid to report a cure for cancer was once found by using Rife's frequency medicine. The forbidden treatment was "off limits" for the mainstream press. Rife may be a blazing area of research and internet discussion, but no one in the print press has dared to break the censorship seal. America's mainstream journalists seem to have lost their professional integrity.

But one journalist defied the embargo. His editor backed him up. And the publisher gave the green light. So, on February 12, 2012, in Rife's home city of San Diego -- where he made his historic discoveries and invented his marvelous instruments -- a newspaper gave homage to a true scientific original. It was the first 21st century newspaper to "speak truth to power" and praise Rife's gifts to humanity.

It was the *San Diego Reader* that published the story. The *Reader* is one of the largest alternative newspapers in the country, with an average press run of 90,000 copies, distributed every Wednesday.

The story's title: "Royal Raymond Rife: Into The Micro Beyond" by Jeff Smith. The feature described Rife's invention of a super optical microscope that made visible for the first time living organisms of virus size. The story reported how Rife's frequency instruments painlessly destroyed the micro-organisms that caused many of humanity's deadliest diseases, including cancer. The story told San Diego readers how the medical powers-that-be stopped the development of a new kind of healing technology and therapy.

Gee, maybe someday the mainstream press also will break the ban on informing the American people about what Royal Rife accomplished.

The following exerpts are from Jeff Smith's and the *San Diego Reader's* February 12, 2012 defiant investigative disclosure of what was off limits for the press -- the cancer establishment's dirty cover-up of Rife's work.

"Every third day, each patient sat a few feet from the ray machine for 3 minutes. Spacing of the treatments 'devitalized' the cancer one tissue layer at a time. It also allowed the body to heal and rid itself of toxins."

"Within 3 months, 14 of the 16 cancer patients had recovered. The other 2 had clean bills of health within the next six weeks."

"On May 6, 1938, the *San Diego Evening Tribune* announced that after 18 years of trial and error in his Point Loma lab, Rife had isolated a cancer organism and a means of arresting it. He compared the ray to compatible tuning forks. When one vibrates, sound waves cause the other to vibrate as well."

"Rife may have made discoveries that are still ahead of our time: a super microscope, a noninvasive means of killing viruses, microorganisms changing shape ... "

"The Beam Ray, if real, became an unthinkable threat to established medicine. ('Imagine a universal cure,' an observer writes, that 'makes drugs obsolete.') ... The FDA withheld approval."

After the story was published, San Diego residents commented on what they had learned from the report. Two weeks later, a MzLiz wrote, "We're all BEGGING for a machine like Mr. Rife's. Imagine how far ahead we'd be if we could have used these past 40 years for more research on his findings? This is not just sad, it's criminal."

How about a belated or honorary Pulitzer for Jeff Smith and the *San Diego Reader* newspaper? For courageous defiance of a long-imposed ban and censorship of a great scientist's inventions and a history-changing discovery of a revolutionary healing technology?

John W. Mattingly provided a useful perspective for future generations who will advance Royal Rife's healing of microbial based diseases and even cancer, thus finally stopping the mass slaughter that the current "political class" and "civil service professionals" have allowed. Mattingly's timeless words:

"Rife employed a system of lighting as unknown to microscopy today as it was in the 1930s. It was not simply *uncommon*, it was *unknown*. This was the first and most fundamental technical strike against understanding Rife's microscope and biological discoveries.

"There were a few who were not distracted by Rife's unknown method of lighting. Having a look at his work, they jumped to the next problem, that of their own dogma, which said it is simply impossible to realize such high magnifications and resolutions with light microscopes, and therefore we do not believe what we see.

"Only recently have discoveries been confirmed in biophysics to make it possible to understand the principles by which Rife's microscopes produced magnfications and resolutions so far beyond the limits of conventional light microscopes.

"Rife extrapolated from his lighting technique ,,, that specific electromagnetic frequencies would have a negative effect on specific bacterial forms. There can remain no doubt that Rife demonstrated the correctness of his hypothesis ... new discoveries in biophysics not only explain Rife's principle of illumination, they also explain his process for selective destruction of bacteria. The latter phenomenon is similar to ultra-sonic cleansing, differing in selectivity of wave form and frequency.

"In retrospect, Rife's microscope appears relatively simple and straightforward, ideally suited for observing living specimens. None of the new light scopes can begin to approach the magnification and resolution achieved by Rife ... Rife's work should, by all means, be reexamined *fairly* in light of new knowledge.

SIMPLE IS GOOD.

BUT THE MEDICAL ESTABLISHMENT AND THE CANCER INDUSTRY DON'T LIKE SIMPLE.

THEY LIKE COMPLICATED AND VERY EXPENSIVE PROCEDURES, EXPERIENCE AND PRODUCTS.

RIFE IS SIMPLE.

RIFE IS INEXPENSIVE.

RIFE IS GOOD.

BUT ONLY QUALITY RIFE INSTRUMENTS WORK.

THE RIP-OFF "RIFE" DEVICES ARE WORTHLESS.

BE ADVISED.

12812448R00089

Printed in Great Britain
by Amazon